ERN BAXTER

"I

**THIS BOOK
CAN SAVE YOUR LIFE.**

ALMOST
DIED!"

Contents

Foreword

Ern Baxter is a rare man. His story is a gripping, moving account of what can happen to us when we obey the laws that govern the fate of our bodies—and the inevitable price we pay when we don't.

Although Ern is an exceptional man, his experience is not an exception to the rule. Hundreds of others with all types of degenerative diseases—heart disease, diabetes, hypertension—have, like Ern, had a second chance to live when they could easily have died.

The issues Ern raises in this book must be faced by everyone. His dramatic story provides us all with both a hope and a challenge: Death can be delayed, disease can be prevented, and health can be restored!

Henri Weibe, M.S.

Human life is more than the movement of atoms and molecules within our bodies' cells as they function together "as programmed." Plants and animals also have cells that function in similar harmony. But human life is much more than plant or animal life. Man has a mental and spiritual nature which distinguishes him from other organisms.

Unfortunately, because man possesses a mind and spirit that lower animals and plants do not possess, philosophy and religion have often elevated these aspects to a high plane while degrading the physical body. Yet we must realize that the body is the house in which our mind and soul dwell. It is the vine from which the branches of the mental and spiritual draw their very existence. We must keep our bodies in the best condition possible so that our minds will be able to function at full capacity. As with computers, our "hardware" must be maintained for the "software" to do its job.

We must realize that the maintenance of our health cannot be relegated to the World Health Organization, the local health department, or even to our beloved family physician. As Dr. John W. Farquhar, director of the heart disease program at Stanford Medical School, has said:

> Ill health is not an isolated event; it is the result of an accumulation of abuses, each seemingly inconsequential. Eventually they take their toll. I believe that the individual has to accept responsibility for maintaining his or her own health. No one else can—not a doctor, not a fleet of doctors. In the way we live our daily lives, we either enhance our health or diminish it.

The message of life-style medicine is that an individual reaps what he has sown. The laws of health that govern our bodies are the same as the laws of gravity, thermodynamics, chemistry, and physics, by which our planet and all in it operate. They will determine our health depending upon our observance of them.

It is most rewarding to be involved in assisting nature in her efforts to maintain optimum function in people's lives. No greater pleasure can come to a physician than to see the restoration of someone's total health without daily reliance on powerful medications—virtually all of which have side effects. It is thrilling, then, to know a person who has rediscovered through his own physical suffering the laws of health. Here is the dramatic account of such a man.

George D. Chen, M.D., M.P.H.

Acknowledgements

I would like to express my deep appreciation to the following people for their work on this book:

Don Basham—for his vital role as the main editor.

Dick Leggatt—for his assistance in editing.

Bob Sutton—for the first editing of the manuscript.

Dr. Henry Weibe—for his role in my recovery at Weimar, and also his editing of the manuscript for medical accuracy.

Dr. George Chen—The Director of the Weimar Institute during my treatment.

Dr. Neal—My personal physician while at Weimar and also a special thanks to the remainder of the Weimar staff.

Bob Robinson—and the Integrity Communications Editorial and Production staff.

Kenneth Veltz—for his role in coordinating this entire project.

Wesley Channel—for providing the bibliography.

And a special word of gratitude for my wife, Ruth—for her constant love, support, and encouragement, and for her keen medical knowledge and culinary adeptness that made the critical difference to me.

Acknowledgements

1
Could This Be the End?

The paramedics would not let me move. They hovered over my prostrate body, efficiently checking my pulse, blood pressure, and other vital signs. My wife, Ruth, and some friends watched anxiously from a corner of our bedroom.

"We'd better take you to the hospital—it looks like a little problem with your heart," one of them finally said. "Don't get up—we'll use a stretcher."

The paramedics loaded me gently into the ambulance. One stepped in beside me and took a seat as the other slammed the door shut. As I watched our home disappear into the distance and felt the rising speed of the ambulance, I wondered just how "little" they thought my problem was!

Only minutes earlier, at about 7:00 a.m., I had stepped into my morning shower with no reason to expect the cheerful California sun to be the harbinger of anything but another pleasant summer day in San Diego. I was mentally reviewing my morning schedule of classes at a local Bible institute where I held a teaching post, when I became aware of a strange burning sensation in my chest. I had been experiencing similar pains for some weeks, particularly when I climbed the stairs to my second-floor office; but the discomfort had always subsided after a short rest. This morning, however, the burning persisted with a growing intensity that moved down my left arm and refused to ease even after I had rested on the bed. I summoned Ruth, who then called some friends. They prayed together for me, and then the decision was made to call the paramedics.

I gloomily watched the trees fly past the ambulance window as it screamed its way through the winding hills to the Pomerado Hospital in Poway, California. Was this the end of the race for me? Was I in some final stage of physical degeneration that would ultimately claim my life? Would I never again preach the glories of the gospel? Was I being set aside now, with still so much yet to do? An invalid at sixty-four years of age, doomed to useless inactivity?

I was not afraid to die, but neither was I eager! It was not the thought of losing my own life or health that grieved me so much as the loss of any remaining years of fruitfulness and service to God and His kingdom.

As the ambulance swerved through halted traffic, I found myself beseeching the Lord to grant me a few more years. Yet even as I prayed, I had the growing and uneasy conviction that if the Lord were to grant me a "stay of execution," some radical changes in life-style were in store for me. I knew I would have to begin to take a far greater measure of responsibility for my ailing physical body and its weary and failing heart, which was struggling so hard to continue beating that June 12, 1979.

My boyhood ambition had certainly not been to weigh three hundred pounds when I grew up. Quite the contrary, when I was married at age twenty-two, I stood a strapping 6' 2½" at a lean 157 pounds. I was called "Skinny" by many of my friends. From my earliest years, I had been athletically inclined, regularly involving myself in any available physical competition. In high school I was avidly involved in body building, making it a point to be on as many athletic teams as possible. Even in those days, something inside me wanted to "run the race"—I was active in football, basketball, soccer, and hockey, and was proud of my ability to hold my own in stiff competition.

But in those early years I also experienced my first taste of the physical penalties that could be reaped from rebellion and disobedience to God. In my late teens, I stormed into the period, which many teenagers experience, of rebellion against God, parents, and all institutions.

My spiritual rebellion came out of my experience with "religion." I was baptized as an infant in the Presbyterian Church, but later my mother, along with my grandmother and my two aunts, converted to a strict Christian sect. This greatly offended my father, who was Presbyterian, and he threatened to leave her. He was a proud, budding young executive who had been brought over from Scotland by the Canadian Bank of Commerce with prospects for a banking future. Of course, he wanted to maintain a life-style that was consistent with his executive position and ambitions, and the Presbyterian Church was the most prestigious church in the city. But in the end he relented and joined my mother's church, and that is where I had my

3

boyhood religious training. It was terribly legalistic. My main understanding of religion at that point was that I must accomodate to a code of externalities, such as the length of the ladies' skirts and the evils of movies and cards. I desperately tried to measure up to the standard, but of course I had no spiritual dynamic to motivate me. I do not want to be unfair to that church or what it represented; I simply want to say what my reactions were to its teachings.

To make matters worse, when I was about fourteen, a pentecostal evangelist came to town. His was a powerful ministry, filled with signs and wonders. Along with hundreds of others, my parents were swept up in the revival he held and became members of the pentecostal church that grew out of that revival. But I was still hung up on externalism, so I decided I would renounce the whole Christian scene.

I remember how deliberate it was—I had tried to serve God, I had tried to be a Christian, but it was not working. I couldn't make it. I wasn't going to pretend to play the game. So one Sunday morning I decided I would stop trying to be a Christian, period. I didn't announce this to anybody, and I went to the service that morning with my father. They were serving the Lord's Supper, and when the elements were offered to me, I declined. After the service my father and I were walking home. We walked in silence for several blocks and then in his booming Scottish voice he remarked, "Boy, you didn't take communion this morning!"

I said, "No, sir!"

"Have you lost your salvation?"

"Yes, sir," I said. And I meant it.

At that point I turned my whole life over to the very

4

opposite of everything I had tried to be before. I thought, "I didn't make being a Christian go. I'll sure make not being a Christian go." So at age fourteen I became a rebel to the core, in the process causing my parents considerable distress.

At seventeen, I was felled by a very severe case of pneumonia. In those days there were no miracle drugs, and when I finally began to recover, the doctor warned me emphatically to be slow and careful during my convalescence. Most of all, he said, I must not go out at nights. But in my rebellion, I disobeyed and sneaked out a couple of times. As a result, I suffered a severe relapse which put me back in bed for several months, worse off than ever.

My parents shared their concern for me with some of the people in the church, and one young man asked permission to come and see me. So they arranged for him to come. Outwardly I was very tough, but inwardly I was scared stiff. I knew I was away from God, but I didn't want to go back to the kind of God that I had left in the first place. So this young man came to see me. I remember quite clearly how he sat down on the side of my bed and began to talk to me. I gave him short answers; I wasn't even civil—largely because I didn't want to get hooked again. I had suffered enough religious confusion.

As we conversed he could tell I wasn't about to give in. So he came right to the point. "Ern," he said, *"being a Christian is not what you do for God, it's what God in Christ Jesus has done for you."* I can remember how his words literally stunned me. I couldn't remember having heard that basic truth before.

Later, I asked my father, "Dad, was I just deaf or did

I never hear that before?"

He said, "Son, you never heard it before."

Well, I didn't let the young man know that he had reached me, but even as I listened to his steps retreating down the stairs I was already doing business with God. "God," I said, "if what he says is true, then I'm your boy. I'm a moral, physical, and spiritual mess, and only You can help me." The instant I said that, I experienced a tremendous spiritual sensation and knew that something redemptive had transpired. I was certain God had heard me. I wasn't going to say anything about it, but later when I came down to the kitchen to talk with my mother, she looked me straight in the eyes. "How are you getting along?" she asked. I tried to be casual about it, but she knew something had happened. To make a long story short, I was miraculously healed.

During the time of my rebellion I had gone into music. It was something I enjoyed and I had been planning to attempt a musical career. It was all I had to offer God so I said, "God, I don't know what this all means, but I offer You my life and my music."

Within a few months a traveling preacher came through town, a church planting pioneer. He needed somebody with musical ability. So I joined his team.

The year was 1932 and I was eighteen years old. Within four months I had received the baptism in the Holy Spirit and realized I could not only serve God with my music, but that God had called me to preach. Immediately after my healing and becoming involved in Christian service, I once more entered into a strenuous life, determined to maintain my health, and to guard the well-being of my physical body. I was slim and well-conditioned, and proud of it.

Then, at age twenty-two, I married. The contentment of a happy marriage and the discontinuance of much of my physical activity coupled with a regular schedule of heavy meals produced some decided physical changes. The nickname "Skinny" ceased to be applicable. My weight rose to over two hundred pounds, and the preaching ministry I was pursuing required long hours of study and a sedentary life-style not designed to maintain either good physical muscle tone or a metabolic rate sufficient to burn off excess calories.

I now had "nobler" pursuits than the "frivolity" of physical competition and excercise. When my friends commented on my increased weight, I jokingly replied I was "enlarging my borders." Public concern over the dangers of obesity was not prevalent in those days, so I found no cause for alarm at my ever-expanding waistline.

My first faint inkling of the severity of my overweight condition came when I went for a physical examination to qualify for a life insurance policy. The physician was sharp and direct. As I sat naked on the examining table, he poked my protruding abdomen with an accusing forefinger and curtly warned that my bulging belly would undoubtedly make the insurance policy I planned to purchase much more expensive. Already humbled by my exposed condition, I lamely replied that I didn't eat all *that* excessively, even though I did weigh almost two hundred fifty pounds.

My feeble effort at self-justification only increased the disgust in the doctor's voice. "Come now, Baxter," he said. "You're an intelligent man. Everything sticking out there," he poked at my paunch once more, "first went through there," and he moved the accusing finger

7

in the direction of my mouth. He was right on both counts. My obesity was the result of undisciplined over-eating and, just as he had predicted, the insurance company penalized me by increasing my premiums. So, although I was in my early twenties, I was already pay-ing for my physical indisciplines—though at that time I thought my loss was only in dollars. I did not know I was also paying my first installments on an ever-in-creasing physical deficit that would leave me with a bankrupt body.

While my disquieting encounter with the doctor gave me temporary cause for thought, it accomplished no permanent change in my life-style. I was quickly dis-tracted by my success in the Lord's work.

As the years progressed, the church I was pastoring continued to grow and prosper. With my ministerial success came an increasing number of opportunities to minister outside my local church. By the time I was thirty-four, I was traveling the world as a Bible teacher with the famous evangelist and miracle worker, Wil-liam Branham. While my ministry was expanding be-yond anything I had ever dreamed, unfortunately so was my girth. My weight had increased to two hundred ninety-six pounds.

Today, when I look at pictures of myself taken during that period, I am rightfully embarrassed. My gross overweight had ceased to be a joke or even amusing as my abused body at last began to register its protest. A small hernia appeared next to my navel as a result of the continued physical strain. In addition, I kept bottles of antacids constantly handy to control my nagging heart-burn. The young man who only ten years before could exercise with energy to spare found himself gasping for

8

air after dragging his excessive body up a single flight of stairs to his office. Finally, I became aware that if I didn't do something about changing my life-style I was going to be in serious trouble. I confessed to my wife, "If I don't do something about this weight, it's going to kill me." When she suggested that I see a doctor I readily agreed.

The medical help I received, however, proved a dubious blessing at best. The drug prescribed for me by the doctor was a powerful stimulant commonly used for weight control. It took off the weight but it also added to my physical discomfort by giving me sleepless nights and by doing strange, indescribable things to my nervous system. While I lost one hundred pounds, I also lost a great deal of my composure and sense of well-being. My sleep pattern was chronically disturbed and my erratic nervous system left me jumpy, irritable, and unable to concentrate. I generally felt at loose ends with myself.

While I felt considerably better without all that extra poundage, unfortunately I hadn't really found the "cure." Even though I never again put on that much weight, I repeatedly journeyed up and down the scales in frustrating cycles over the next few years. But most of my spasmodic attempts at weight control were motivated more from a desire to avoid a stroke or heart attack than from a scriptural understanding of God-glorifying moderation and discipline.

I was a hardy subscriber to a popular approach to ministry (which I will elaborate on later) which simply never considered physical problems to be the result of disobedience to biblical instruction on the proper treatment of the body. Beyond my ignorance, I could point to

9

many of my ministerial heros, both ancient and modern, who were "big" preachers. Later I saw quite clearly that some of these giants of the faith would have lived longer in the service of the Lord if they had treated their bodies with biblical care.

I had become one of the overweight preachers who were a common sight in the 1940's and 50's even as they are today. I had fallen into a ministerial life-style common to many men of the cloth. Let me describe a typical daily schedule—one which, with only minor variations, would aptly fit thousands of businessmen, executives, and other professionals as well.

The faithful servant of the Lord drags himself from bed after a short night's sleep, into the embrace of an eye-opening cup of coffee and a sugar-coated, pop-toasted, sweet nothing for breakfast. Or worse, he has no breakfast at all. Morning at the church office provides the ever-present cup of coffee from the resident coffee pot constantly available for refills.

Noon for the pastor usually signifies lunch with some important committee, or else with one of his parishioners at a restaurant or steak house where the meals are long on fats, starch, and sugar and short on breathable air, peace, and quiet.

Returning to the office sluggish and sleepy, his afternoon affords another round of coffee or caffeinated colas from the church refrigerator. The stress of church administration, visits from problem-laden parishioners, and preparation for evening meetings all combine with repeated jolts of caffeine to produce adrenal exhaustion by 4:30 in the afternoon. By 5:00 p.m. the heavy-eyed preacher finds his way home where he kisses his wife on the cheek and pats his children on the head before heading to the bedroom where he "collapses" for thirty or forty minutes of blissful unconsciousness prior to the evening meal.

Dinner at the parsonage is often a social event. Tonight's visitors are Deacon Smith and his wife. That means a full-course dinner heaped onto an already overburdened digestive system still trying to rid itself of the hamburger and fries it has been struggling with since lunch. Is tonight lasagna or fried chicken? Whatever the cuisine, second helpings are always in order. And of course, Mrs. Smith brought along her pastor's favorite dessert—pecan pie topped with mounds of whipped cream!

It's no less a hazard when the preacher and his wife visit the parishioner's home for dinner. It is always a special occasion for the family to have the pastor and his wife share a meal. The parade of irresistible culinary taste-thrillers is a genuine expression of their love and appreciation of his faithful ministry.

After dinner, the pastor leaves for another meeting carrying the burden of a floundering digestive system and trudging blood stream which must somehow handle hundreds of unneeded calories of fat and sugar. The evening meeting will provide some temporary relief. However, by the time the meeting is over at 10:00 p.m., the emotional letdown he experiences at the end of a hectic day may be accompanied by still more food with a few friends at the local fast-food chain, where the fare may be anything from pepperoni pizza to hot fudge sundaes. Even if he heads straight home, there awaits the customary dish of ice cream or glass of milk with a hearty pile of cookies to be consumed in front of the late-night TV news.

By this late hour some pastors are so keyed up from the stressful day and the repeated assaults of caffeine that they find it necessary to follow Paul's admonition to Timothy, "take a little wine for your stomach's sake." Of course, the last thing the stomach needs is a glass of wine, but if something doesn't unwind their revving nervous system, they will never get to sleep. And even when they do finally sleep, there is little rest for a digestive system that must still handle the final contribution of the day's caloric excess.

Only in the early hours of the morning will the stomach finally be able to rest for an hour or two before it is bludgeoned into another day's activity by the morning's first gulp of hot coffee with its load of acid and caffeine.

I kidded myself into believing the personal late-night routine of indulgence was just compensation for a malnourished childhood coupled with having to walk, underfed, several miles to and from school in harsh winter weather. The need for compensation manifested itself with amazing regularity at bedtime every night. It took the form of an overwhelming craving for either peppermint candy or ice cream or better yet, the two in combination.

Finally my dear wife, Ruth, who is a registered nurse, drew upon her medical expertise and provided an even more precise diagnosis of the true problem. "Ern," she complained one day, "I think you must have at least two extra glands—a peppermint gland and an ice cream gland—and you're constantly feeding both of them!"

Obviously, she was right! And I just knew that depriving one's glands could produce serious physical and mental—not to mention spiritual—consequences!

Thereafter I was diligent to satiate both glands whenever they acted up even in the slightest. Just to make sure I would never be caught in a vulnerable position, I took care to see that a permanent stash of peppermint candy was hoarded away underneath my bed just in case one of those glands complained after I had retired. This would spare me the inconvenience of walking all the way to the kitchen, or of having to deny my craving until the next day.

Many of you find yourselves smiling at what I have just recounted, but for some it will be a painful smile of self-recognition, because examples of such an overindulgent life-style are all around us. Others may argue that my description is grossly exaggerated, but I have lived too long to forsake the description; it is tragically applicable to too many of us. While I may have slightly embellished the account for the purpose of illustration, even the less exaggerated life-style common to almost every Christian leader I know will have the same terminal (I use the word intentionally!) effect. And I must repeat—lest anyone feel left out—*that with only minor variations the same picture I have painted aptly fits thousands of businessmen, executives, and professionals I know.*

I continued to embrace the self-indulgent life-style I have just described until 1957, when I was felled by a coronary insufficiency (forerunner of a major heart attack). While my body's cry of alarm during that crisis jolted me into a temporary period of moderation, I must painfully confess that within months I began to slip once more into the same old pattern: keeping my body laboring along with drugs and trespassing on God's grace, without really giving heed to the pleas for mercy from a body steadily wearing down.

The next twenty years brought only slight change in my life-style. My body continued to perform its function of getting my spirit and soul where I wanted them with only spasmodic complaints or breakdowns. I had developed what I thought was a good arrangement with my body: As long as it got me where I wanted to go with a minimum of fuss and interference, I would keep it pampered, spoiled, and indulged. *Never once during the physical ups and downs of those years did I hear a clear voice from Christian leaders on the biblical significance of the physical body and its need for discipline and care!* Only heaven will ever fully compute the loss of time, usefulness, and well-being caused by my own lack of personal physical discipline.

Entrance into my sixties found little left in my bank of physical reserve to make the continued installment payments I had begun so many years before. The deficit was too big—a crash was inevitable.

2
Real Trouble This Time

By the spring of 1979 I knew I was in serious physical trouble. The preceding year had been increasingly discouraging as I had watched the accelerating degeneration of my health. One of the first and most frightening symptoms was blurred vision. As a lifelong student I was an avid reader, and few things could strike fear in my heart faster than the possibility of losing my eyesight. I made an appointment with the ophthalmologist. He gave my eyes a thorough examination and found nothing wrong with them, but suggested I be checked for diabetes. After a series of blood and metabolic tests, the diabetes specialist's diagnosis confirmed the eye doctor's suspicion. I was diabetic. This was my first real introduction to a very simple but painful truth: <u>If your life-style does not control your body, eventually your body will control your life-style.</u> Now my failing systems were forcing changes upon me. I was immediately introduced to the diabetic's way of life—radical restriction of sugars and the daily injection of insulin to regulate my metabolism.

But my diabetic condition was only part of the bad news I received from my blood analysis. The cholesterol (a fat-related substance) and triglyceride (saturated fat) levels in my blood were also seriously elevated. The physician warned me that these elevated blood levels and the diabetic condition were a common companion of cardiovascular disease. I was a prime candidate for a stroke and/or heart attack. I had to face the sober truth that my bloodstream was carrying a potentially lethal cargo of illegal explosives, apt to detonate at any time, and my constantly high blood pressure was a warning of how seriously my heart was being taxed in pumping this turgid sludge through my veins.

As if all these alarming reports were not enough, I felt half sick most of the time. Dizziness, sleeplessness, weakness, and other debilitating physical irregularities were making my life only barely tolerable. And those conditions were certainly not helped by the excess weight I was carrying, added pounds which were also sapping my energy and imposing extra labor on my already overworked heart.

In retrospect, I behaved like a man bent on scheduling his own funeral. In spite of my beleaguered body's headlong plunge toward the point of total surrender, I continued my full work regimen. In fact, I added to my already busy teaching and traveling schedule by assuming a teaching post with a full schedule of classes at a Bible institute in San Diego, California. As these new responsibilities settled onto my already drooping shoulders, I sensed deep inside that something was about to snap.

During those days a young married couple close to Ruth and me were deeply concerned over my deteriorating physical condition and urged me to consider the treatment available at Weimar Institute, near Sacramento, California. The wife had been stricken with cardiovascular problems similar to mine and had experienced a remarkable recovery under Dr. Zane P. Kime, the medical advisor to the Institute. They had seen others of their friends helped, and were sure that I would greatly benefit from the Institute's program. The Weimar Institute, they assured us, was run by a fully qualified medical staff of doctors, nurses, and technicians. Though the Institute used the best available modern medical technology, their emphasis was on naturally restoring the body to a state of maximum strength and recuperative potential through proper understanding and application of nutrition, exercise, and rest.

So convinced were our friends that we would benefit from Weimar's unique treatment program that they offered to underwrite the cost. I must admit that even though we became quite convinced of Weimar's benefits by the time we signed up, in our initial conversations with our friends I had a few misgivings. I had some vague beliefs about the benefits of "health food" and "eating right," but the idea of a full-blown institute about nothing but nutrition seemed a bit extreme. I could conjure up visions of gaunt, beady-eyed, unshorn and unbathed hippies, who lived in trees without the benefits of civilized convenience or restraint, and who subsisted on roots, berries, and strange herbal teas, which—whenever I had had the misfortune to encounter them—always vaguely reminded me of stale hay.

Nevertheless, the obvious benefits to our friend soon convinced Ruth and me of Weimar's credibility, and we gratefully accepted and applied for admission. We were scheduled to attend one of the Institute's twenty-six-day sessions as soon as the school term ended. Unfortunately, however, the collision course I had set for my body years before was rapidly coming to a climax, and the scheduled trip to Weimar was not to be.

By early June I was beginning to experience some new discomfort in my chest. Climbing to my second-floor school office had for some time occasioned a shortness of breath and burning chest pains. Usually, after a brief rest the pain would subside and I could continue my activities with only minimal difficulty. A little more troubling, however, was a new brand of pains which were beginning to appear, somewhat sharper, near my heart. These pains would show up at inopportune times which were not necessarily related to extended expenditures of energy.

Of course, the appearance of the more frequent chest pains, along with the general physical disintegration I was experiencing, had a considerable emotional impact. To find myself feeling miserable most of the time and just barely able to perform the basic physical activities of life, left me disheartened and demoralized. I could see myself falling behind in the race of life with a vast field of runners moving on past me toward the final laps. While I had absorbed enough spiritual mellowness over the years to keep from becoming truly angry or resentful at my situation, nevertheless it was deeply disappointing to be looking toward finishing my life's course with enthusiasm and excitement, only to helplessly watch my faltering body be disqualified from the race. The worst of these increasing chest pains interrupted my shower that morning on June 12, 1979, with the un-

18

scheduled ambulance ride to the hospital.

Upon my arrival at the hospital, a cardiologist was summoned and I was given an EKG as well as numerous other tests. No definite problems were pinpointed, but unquestionably, something was wrong.

In order to get an accurate picture of exactly what my heart was doing, the specialists attached a monitor to me that would keep tabs on my heart's every beat, awake or asleep, over the course of my stay in the hospital.

After three days of observation and appropriate medication, the specialist concluded that I had not had a "heart attack" as such—but my "spell" was so close to a heart attack it was evident that I definitely had serious problems. At least my blood pressure, which was alarmingly elevated at my admission, had stabilized and the medication seemed to be controlling my "angina," which I was later to learn was the technical term for my particular brand of chest pains. In men my age and physical condition, angina is almost always occasioned by distress of the heart muscles when they are receiving an insufficient supply of blood to furnish oxygen for normal activity. This insufficiency is usually the result of some type of obstruction or blockage in the coronary artery of the heart, which is its main source of blood supply.

I was released from the hospital with the understanding that if the angina persisted I would have to undergo an angiogram, a procedure doctors use to check the condition of the blood vessels supplying the heart. In light of the facts I was to learn later about my heart condition, I now realize that the cardiologists were already suspecting that there was some type of blockage in my coronary artery.

We cancelled our Weimar appointment for July 1, since I had to remain close to my heart specialist. We cancelled with regret, hoping to go at some future date.

When the angina persisted in spite of medication, limited activity, and prayer, my cardiologist insisted on doing an angiogram to determine the extent of my problem. The news came as quite a shock.

The human mind has a marvelous mechanism for rationalizing and submerging the reality of serious physical problems. In spite of all the painful symptoms, for months I had been able to brush aside most of my deepest concern by assuming that somehow I would eventually "get over it"; that with a little more rest or some new medication the crisis would pass. Now, my defenses were crumbling like a sand castle at the tide's edge, and the stark reality of my degenerating condition loomed larger and larger.

My trip to the hospital for the angiogram prompted some real soul-searching. I loved the Lord and I did not want to dishonor Him in this difficult trial by doubting His faithfulness to me or His perfect purposes for my life. But in spite of all the faith and assurance I tried to muster, I found myself accepting with fatalistic resignation the facts of my advancing age, the mortal nature of the fleshly body, and what I had known of the experience of others in my condition. At sixty-five years of age should I really be surprised to find my abused heart in serious trouble?

Having the angiogram turned out to be an amazing experience for me. Although it was a surgical process, the angiogram would not be done under general anesthesia, and I would thus be able to watch the procedures. What order and efficiency! I watched the proficient medical team perform exact roles with precise timing under the expert authority of the doctor. My life, like that of any patient on the operating table, depended on the efficient teamwork of the surgical staff. As I watched the marvelous cooperation of the team, I wondered how many souls or "patients" had been lost to the body of Christ because of a lack of proper supportive teamwork by the various "physicians" of the body of Christ. In a strange sort of way, watching the procedure gave me a glimmer of hope in an otherwise very dark situation. I wanted to press on to achieve some of the goals of spiritual order and teamwork which I had pursued for so many years.

A local anesthetic was administered to the upper inside of my right thigh, and a small incision was made in the large femoral artery which is the main blood supply to the legs. The surgeon inserted a probing tube into the incision and monitored its progress on a fluoroscope as it threaded its way up toward the arteries of my heart. I was able to watch the entire procedure on a television monitor. Once the end of the tube was positioned near my heart, small doses of dye were released into the blood which momentarily caused the arteries to appear like branch-like fingers on the screen. Watching my own heart beating away on a TV screen, with the realization that I had taken for granted its vital function for sixty-five years and it was now in danger, was both fascinating and frightening.

The team's firm hands moved me into different positions on the special hammock-like surgical table, as various pictures were taken to record my heart's "arterial road map." The procedure was completed as effi-

21

ciently as it was begun, and I was wheeled back to my room with only one question in my mind—what would the pictures tell?

The report was less than gratifying. "One of your arteries is about seventy per cent clogged," the doctor told me. "That means part of your heart is receiving only about one third of the normal supply of blood. That's why it complains by giving you angina with even the slightest exertion. I don't think we'll consider surgery immediately," he concluded. "We'll try medications for the present."

The blockage in my coronary artery was due to the build-up of cholesterol on the inside of the artery walls. Like rust building up in an old pipe, the cholesterol restricted the free flow of blood to the muscles of the heart until the shortage became so critical that the complaining heart muscles produced the severe vise-like pain called angina. Should the restricted opening in the arteries become totally obstructed, or if the demands put on the heart muscle become so severe that the limited blood supply can no longer sustain life, then the portion of the heart muscle supplied by that particular artery may die. That death is called a *myocardial infarction*. When this occurs the patient has what is known as a "major" heart attack. If a large enough area of the heart muscle is involved, the patient may die in a few moments. If, however, a smaller area of the heart muscle is affected, then the chances of recovery are improved.

If the cholesterol build-up has continued over a number of years, the chances of totally reversing it are limited since the deposits begin to harden. When this happens doctors usually try a procedure known as "bypass" surgery. They remove a small section of blood vessel from the patient's leg and graft it around the clogged portion of the coronary artery in the patient's heart. Though the procedure is highly successful and fairly routine nowadays, it is still nothing to be approached lightly. The doctors were now considering bypass surgery to relieve my beleaguered heart muscles.

A few days after the angiogram I was released from the hospital with bottles of appropriate medications, including the angina sufferer's ever-present companion—nitroglycerin. Nitroglycerin, which is also one of the primary ingredients of dynamite, dilates or enlarges the blood vessels of the human body, allowing a freer flow of blood. To the heart patient, nitroglycerin can literally be a lifesaver. Enlarging the blood vessels of the heart allows enough blood to reach the oxygen-starved heart muscle to relieve distress and reduce the pain. Since angina attacks are never predictable, the heart patient usually keeps a little bottle of nitroglycerin tablets within easy reach night or day.

The doctors told me to restrict my activities severely for the next six months. I would not be able to resume my school work since I had to "take it easy" and dedicate this period of time to recovery. I was more concerned, however, over what would happen *after* the six months. My cardiologist had mentioned trying several different types of medications and, in all probability, surgery. All in all, I was totally at a loss about what to expect. Maybe the pain wouldn't get any worse—the nitroglycerin had surely helped that. Or maybe God would grant me a gift of healing, as He had often done before. One way or another, I would have to receive each new day as His gift and wait on His mercies, however He led me.

23

As the shock of the crisis subsided, Ruth and I began to consider the Weimar clinic again. The time was definitely available, since I could no longer travel or teach. The only question was whether or not Weimar had room for us at this time. We called them and were grateful to learn they could enter us in the program starting August 26th. Without much hope, I must confess, we started to prepare for our trip to Weimar.

3
The Providence of God

Ruth and I decided to drive to the Weimar Institute from San Diego. We planned a leisurely two-and-a-half day trip up the coast. Of course, we had to pay special attention to my personal pharmacy of medical paraphernalia. Insulin, syringes, and blood pressure medication were all carefully packed—and, most important, we had to make sure the life-saving nitroglycerin was handy in the car to relieve those all too frequent angina attacks.

I wondered at times if going to the Weimar Institute for its twenty-six-day session was really the right step to take. What could the Institute do for me that skilled cardiologists and sophisticated medical techniques could not do? Hadn't the medical professionals who had cared for me up until now told me with authoritative finality not to expect much except more medication and surgery? Perhaps I should have stayed home and nursed my failing strength. At least I could have comforted my soul with prayer and God's Word and special sessions of thanksgiving for nitroglycerin, with the hope of a possible reprieve through open-heart surgery. But in the end

I decided that there could be little harm in finding out what Weimar had to offer.

We were not totally ignorant of what to expect at the Institute. Our friends had shared enough of their experience to give us a general idea of what the treatment would be like. Not knowing exactly what was on the schedule after our arrival, however, we stopped at a McDonald's just a few miles from Weimar for our "last meal"! I ordered a Big Mac and a tall cup of coffee. I wondered if they served hamburgers at Weimar. Little did I know that Big Mac was indeed to be my last meal of that kind!

The unobtrusive road sign read "Weimar Institute: Health Conditioning Center," and the iron gates at the entrance opened onto pleasant, tree-graced grounds. The Weimar Institute is located on three hundred forty acres of beautiful countryside, occupying buildings that had once housed a tubercular hospital. That day reminded me of my first physical collapse at age sixteen with pneumonia. Could I expect God to be as gracious to me now as He had been so many years before?

As we parked the car and approached the main office, I was relieved that everyone we saw was relatively normal-looking. No hippies or far-out people thus far. I did notice, however, how thin and trim all the staff members were! At once I felt out of place.

"Reverend and Mrs. Baxter," the nurse smiled as we entered, "we're so glad to have you as our guests. Won't you come this way, please?" A physical exam was part of our registration process. The nurse strapped on the blood pressure cuff and pumped it up. She could not completely hide the alarmed look she shot at Ruth as she took the reading, but she made determined small

26

talk as she continued her procedures. That little scene did nothing to help my depression! We later learned that my blood pressure was 180/110—alarmingly high. The scales were not too kind, either—223 pounds. I could tell I was off to an impressive start!

We were given preliminary orientation, and prepared for blood and stress tests which were scheduled for the next day. Our accommodations were quite comfortable. Weimar had built a large dormitory-style complex with each room furnished like a hotel room, with private bath and entrance. I began to think that maybe the Institute might be a tolerable place for a rest after all.

The first morning began with blood tests and a session on the treadmill to check the condition of my heart. The technicians strapped me onto an EKG machine to monitor my heart activity, and I began walking on the treadmill at a moderate pace. I had proceeded only a discouragingly short distance when I began breathing laboriously and experiencing an intensifying tightness in my chest. The technicians and doctors convened momentarily over the monitor, and, to my relief, announced that I could step off and sit down.

That afternoon we had our first visit with our assigned doctor. We were to meet with him twice a week during our entire stay as he continually monitored our progress and made any needed adjustments in our treatment. He began by reviewing the results of my tests. High blood pressure, overweight, excessive blood cholesterol and triglycerides, high blood sugar, signs of coronary insufficiency on the treadmill test, diabetes—on and on it went! Finally he put down his papers and looked us straight in the eye, saying: *"But all that can be changed."* I could scarcely believe his words.

To say the least, I was doubtful. The best medical men on the West Coast had already sealed my fate, and now this man claimed Weimar could reverse my downhill plummet. But I was either too skeptical or too worn out to argue with him, so I kept silent, nodding my head politely. I would wait and see.

The doctor gave us each personalized schedules which outlined the diet and exercise programs we would be following during our stay. He stated very simply and clearly the goal of the program for me: a normal blood profile and the first stages of a reversal of my heart problems!

"Now," he concluded, "I hope you will enjoy your stay here as our guests. Can we just have a word of prayer together before you leave?"

I had been in literally dozens of doctor's offices in my life, but only on one or two occasions had they ever offered to pray with me, and then the doctor was a close Christian brother. But this doctor, a total stranger, prayed fervently for me. He expressed his trust in the Lord for His strength and guidance, and thanked Him for His mercy in provision. The prayer was simple, but it left me with a sense that the man assigned as my personal physician was confident, peaceful, and assured about his work. He clearly had a genuine trust in and dependence on the Lord. I thanked him warmly and we set out for our rooms to read up on our schedules.

The next morning we headed for the cafeteria where the whole institute met together for meals. My mouth was watering for a healthy portion of eggs, bacon, hash brown potatoes, and buttered toast or biscuits. Most of all I was ready for the hot cup of life-giving coffee which I had missed the previous morning since we had fasted breakfast in preparation for our blood tests. The breakfast menu was a decided shock. Oatmeal with raisins and fresh fruit? Was that all? And no coffee! Anyone in his right mind knows you can't start the day without coffee! These people had gone too far! If I was to die here, I should at least be able to enjoy myself!

"Oh well," I sighed, "at least we can fill up on oatmeal and fruit."

"Check your sheet," Ruth said. "One thousand calories a day. And no second helpings!" No wonder everyone here was so slim! I had the feeling our stay might seem longer than I had anticipated. Besides the oatmeal with raisins and fresh fruit we had a special whole wheat bread, which we were later to learn was made without sugar or oil. On the bread we had a portion of "jam" which was also made without sugar. All *that* I might handle, but I wasn't sure about not having coffee. I checked the serving line twice to make sure there wasn't a steaming pot-full somewhere which I had somehow overlooked. No luck.

"I don't suppose there might be some juice to drink?" I asked Ruth. Another look at the instruction sheet confirmed my fears. "No fluid one-half hour before meals and none for one hour after. In between drink eight to ten glasses of water." Strange indeed! After the meager breakfast I had difficulty convincing my stomach we had really been there. "Maybe lunch will be better," I thought as we set off for chapel.

Chapel services were held twice daily for those who cared to attend. Ruth and I did, and always found the inspirational messages uplifting. The talks centered around part of the Institute motto, "Trust in divine power." The messages were kept simple and non-sectarian, but they never failed to provide something that we needed for the day.

Chapel gave us a chance to digest breakfast, and then we changed into our shorts and sneakers for group calisthenics. The workout periods were not strenuous—mostly stretching and bending—and they seemed rather pleasant in the fresh air and sun. I tired quickly, however, and was glad when they were over.

I had begun to notice the condition of some of the other participants at the Institute. Many were in far worse shape than I was, and were not even able to participate in the group exercises. I should have been grateful for the strength I did have left.

We went straight from the calisthenics session to physical therapy, where a personalized exercise program awaited us. Besides exercising for a general toning up, I concentrated on strengthening my legs and performing general cardiorespiratory exercise.

In physical therapy I had my first encounter with the exercise bicycle. This contraption was not only designed to condition my legs and hips, but to give my heart and lungs a workout as well. Prominently situated on the handle bars were a speedometer and an odometer. We were required to attain a certain speed and then hold that pace for a designated distance. I had not quite reached a mile when the tightness started in my chest and the physical theraptist told me we had gone far enough for that day. "Don't be discouraged," she said. "It takes most of our guests a few days to get used to exercising on the bicycle." Judging from my discouraging performance, it was going to take me a lot longer than "a few days."

By now I had noticed that we were never referred to

as "patients"; we were always "guests." That was nice, I thought. Our therapist prayed a simple but sincere prayer with us and sent us on our way to the next session. Prayer again! The invocation of divine strength and blessing was part of each session with every therapist or doctor throughout our stay. I came to appreciate the strength and confidence of those simple prayers more and more as our treatment at the Institute continued.

Physical therapy was followed by hydrotherapy, which utilized various sessions of whirlpools and showers. They were quite relaxing and invigorating after the exercise period, and I enjoyed them immensely.

The last hour and a half of the morning was rounded out with a medical lecture. The doctors used simple charts and drawings to explain the rationale of the treatment and to give us additional understanding about our physical systems so that we could appreciate the philosophy behind the Institute's program.

The first lecture was fairly general, explaining the nutritional programs and what we could expect from the exercise regimen. The nutritional program at the Institute was built around this slogan: "At breakfast you eat like a king, at lunch you eat like a queen, and at dinner you eat like a pauper."

"If today's breakfast was for a king," I mused, "then we can skip dinner, because it won't be there!"

Time for lunch! Quite hungry by now, I approached the dinner hall with anticipation, desperately hoping the queen would fare better than the king. We were served a salad, two vegetables, and a small portion of beans! I tried to savor the fare as much as possible, but memories of the Big Mac I had eaten just a scant forty-eight hours before kept floating before my eyes. My mouth watered just thinking about it! I took another bite of beans.

Of course, we still were served no coffee or tea. The medical lecture had put to rest once and for all any false hopes I had had—caffeine in any form was *strictly "verboten!"*

After lunch we could take a rest or go hiking. A few stouter souls hit the trail while I retreated to my bed to console my disgruntled stomach.

The rest of the afternoon was rounded out with different group classes and sessions. They added insult to injury by including a cooking class in the program. Listening to lectures on food for an hour and a half while the walls of your stomach are rubbing blisters on one another is sheer torture. But the cooking class was aimed at orienting us toward a totally new way of cooking that would eliminate unhealthful foods from our diet, and maximize the nutritional value of the foods we did eat. After the cooking class, at 4:00 p.m., we had a second chapel session for those who wanted to attend. As with the morning session, we made attendance our regular habit.

At 6:00 p.m. I found myself seated in the dining hall staring glumly at the "dinner" on my plate. Two pieces of fresh fruit and a slice of bread. They weren't kidding when they said dinner was for a pauper! The paupers never had any chance of sneaking back for seconds, either. Staff members policed the meal to make sure no one departed from their regimen by so much as a calorie. I concluded that by the time we reached the end of our twenty-six day stay, if my heart had not failed first, starvation would kill me. Either way, the future looked bleak.

After another lecture on nutrition which ended about 9:30, we headed for bed. Here I was to mourn the demise of my beloved bedtime "snack period." My peppermint and ice cream "glands," which up to this point had been merely sulking, now began to register formal protests. I had scarcely realized how much of my eating was pure habit until I tried to make a sudden adjustment in it. I was surprised how difficult going to bed without my nocturnal nibbles could be. For me, eating was as much a part of retiring as putting on my pajamas and brushing my teeth. Feeling generally miserable, I retreated between the sheets, hoping to find a little comfort in unconciousness.

I slept poorly, as had been my pattern for some time. Poor health, travel, general physical discomfort, and multitudes of medications had conspired to keep me from enjoying a sound, uninterrupted night's sleep for many years. Tonight, however, my gnawing hunger added to the general discomfort and kept me more restless and fitful than usual.

Mornings at Weimar began at 6:00 a.m. sharp, with a walk around the Institute grounds. By the second morning, I managed to walk a little over a mile at a moderate pace before the inevitable angina set in. I popped a nitroglycerin under my tongue, sat down, and morosely watched others stride past as I waited for the attack to subside. Once the pain subsided I eased my way to the room to get ready for breakfast, which I endured without enthusiasm.

The bicycle was equally discouraging that morning. I had pedaled my way for little more than a mile before the angina again brought the session to a halt.

"It's useless," I complained to my doctor during my afternoon visit, "I can't even get started on the exercises! I barely begin, and then this angina starts and I have to quit. I'll never make any progress at this rate!"

"Don't become discouraged," he recommended. "Just take your nitroglycerin and keep exercising. You'll get through the pain."*

The very thought of continuing to exercise with the angina tightening its grip around my chest was almost enough to trigger an attack right there in his office! He must have seen the horror on my face and tried to soothe my fears.

"Don't worry; we won't let you do any damage to yourself. You must understand that your angina is an indication of an insufficiency. It is not a heart attack. Your nitroglycerin will open your arteries to let sufficient blood get through to prevent damage. If you keep walking, the pain will pass and you will begin to strengthen your heart muscle and improve the quality of its circulation. Eventually, you should be able to walk without any pain at all."

The advice was easy for him to give, I thought, *but he didn't have the pain!* He convinced me to try, however, reminding me there were always trained people handy on the walking track to help out if I got in trouble. Any-

---

*This was the doctor's counsel to me. My understanding is that others are counseled differently according to their particular physical condition. No aspect of my treatment is necessarily applicable to others; at the Institute, each guest receives treatment tailored to his specific needs. Since persisting in exercise beyond the point of heart pain could be dangerous, I urge readers not to attempt it without the advice of a physician.

way, I had until the next morning before I would have to face the ordeal again.

By now I realized that I had an unjustified fear of my angina. Whenever the pain struck, I would flee to a prone position, sucking on a nitroglycerin tablet until the attack passed. I'm sure that the stress caused by the sheer terror of the angina only made the pain worse. My need for nitroglycerin had increased to the point that I would often rub a nitroglycerin paste on my chest, then cover the paste with cellophane. This procedure kept a trickle of nitroglycerin entering my blood stream all the time and did wonders to alleviate my pain. Perhaps I would be wise to rub on a healthy portion before my walk the next morning.

The third day was the most miserable yet. In addition to everything else I had a continuous headache, a general listlessness, and the ever-present *HUNGER*. I kept thinking about that Big Mac. How could I possibly endure twenty-three more days of this treatment?

That third evening was the crisis point. Only later would I fully understand all that was going on in my body, but on that evening I only knew that my body was screaming. Several things were buffeting me simultaneously. Having been a heavy coffee drinker for many years, I knew the sudden cessation of caffeine was afflicting my body with painful symptoms of withdrawal. My headache increased in intensity until it was throbbing in every inch of my skull, a torment which severely increased my general feeling of depression and weakness. I had given up taking the numerous medications for my various infirmities, with the exception of those which were critical for my vital functioning, so my body was showing a number of withdrawal symptoms from

35

these drugs as well. I had not slept well since arriving, and having to arise at 6:00 a.m. had left me with a physical exhaustion which further accentuated my misery. To top off my afflictions, I was ravenous with hunger! My stomach continually growled in spasms, and I could not stop thinking about something to eat. I kept having vivid mental images of big rich meals followed by sweet, gooey desserts!

I would later learn that my whole system was undergoing a dramatic metabolic change. My body had been used to running, albeit poorly, on sugar, fat, refined starch, and caffeine. Now I was having to get used to whole grains, whole grain breads and cereals, fruits, and vegetables—and only a thousand calories a day of them. In many ways, I was in a situation similar to the early stages of a fast when the body begins to live on its own stored fat rather than the food that is eaten. The first few days are difficult since the new metabolism must first get started and then begin the process of absorbing and eliminating the toxic material left from the rich foods which had been eaten before. The cleansing process is quite unpleasant. I was weak, dizzy, nauseated at times, and generally ill.

I lay in bed suffering and fidgeting, trying to get to sleep. Finally, I flung the covers off the bed and began pacing up and down the floor, taking my misery out on Ruth.

"Whose idea was it to come here in the first place?" I stormed.

"Yours, dear." Ruth offered meekly.

Her helpful insight did little to comfort me.

"Did you pack anything for me to eat?" I knew I was behaving like a junky needing a fix.

"No, dear. You know we weren't supposed to bring in any food."

"Well, I don't care! Go and get me something to eat," I demanded. "I'm starving to death!"

"Where?"

"I don't know," I groaned. "The kitchen, I guess! Just go!"

She quietly set off, wondering, I'm sure, whom she would find to give her some food and how to explain the whole thing if she did find somebody. Worse yet, what would she do, or what would *I* do, if she couldn't find anyone to give me some sustenance?

What seemed like hours later, she returned with a small sack. I had been fantasizing about another Big Mac, but by now I knew better than to get my hopes up for a hamburger.

"Did you find me something?"

"Yes dear, I did." She sounded a little *too* positive.

"What did you get?"

"Well. . . I found the cook and explained the problem to him, but all he would give me was this." I tore open the paper bag she offered me.

Toast! Dry toast at that! But at least it was something I could chew on! My adjustment to diet food must have been further along than I knew, because those two slices of cold, dry toast tasted as good as the juiciest sirloin steak I had ever eaten.

Fortified by the snack, I decided I should try to get a little rest. Earlier I had seriously considered packing up and sneaking off into the night. Only the fact that our friends had paid for our costs compelled me to stay. Had it been my own money, my escape from such a prison of starvation would have seemed worth the financial loss!

At 6:00 a.m. the next morning we were all congregated at the outdoor track for our morning walk. Feeling slightly better after some sleep, I decided to try walking through my angina as my doctor had suggested, and having affirmed my peace with God, I started out. Somewhere just short of a mile the tightness began. I was sure this was going to be the end. I took my nitroglycerin, slowed my pace slightly, and kept going.

The pain got worse...and worse.

I began to pray under my breath and slowed my pace even more.

The attendant nearby told me not to worry and to keep going. The pain was everlastingly steady. Finally, the discomfort began to ease, only slightly at first, and then more and more.

To my amazement the longer I walked the better I felt.

I had done it!

I ended up walking over two miles that morning. I couldn't believe what I had just done. Suddenly the day was beautiful!

The stint on the stationary bicycle was another session of working through the attack without stopping. The odometer read one and six tenth miles. My best ride yet.

The fourth day was even better. My headache had subsided significantly and my stomach seemed finally resigned to the spartan fare it would have to live on. At best, life was tolerable again. I breezed through my exercise periods, and that night I went to sleep with only minor difficulty, then slept through most of the night. In fact, I slept better than I had in years.

I had to admit that others at the Institute were suffering far more than I—particularly the "guests" addicted to nicotine. Weimar urged against gradual withdrawals. Combined with everything else they were having to endure, the withdrawals must have been horribly difficult.

The next day, day five, brought another visit to the doctor. Having walked through the angina two mornings in a row, I felt almost smug about my acomplishment.

"Your blood profile is looking good," he said. "Why don't you try stopping the insulin injections?"

I could not have felt more shocked if the doctor had struck me physically! *Give up my insulin?*

My mind flashed back to the doctor who had started me on insulin, and the grave warnings and dire forbodings he had prophesied if I were ever to stop the injections. I was just barely beginning to feel decent again and was certainly not anxious to put my body through any more trauma.

"Well.... I don't know, Doctor...." my voice trailed off.

"I think you'll do fine without it," he replied confidently. "Give it a try."

He always made my major adjustments sound so easy! Well, he had been right about the angina, so maybe I *should* give it up. But then again, why press my luck?

"I'll split the difference," I finally told Ruth. "I'll just take half a dose." I proceeded to give myself the reduced amount. Several hours passed with no noticeable ill efects. Maybe the doctor had been right. Still, no need taking chances. I would stick with my own prescription.

That night I slept even better than the night before, and I awakened feeling genuinely rested. My walk that morning was almost three miles, even with working through a session with the angina. The biggest surprise, however, came when I stepped onto the stationary bicycle. I rode almost four miles and easily went through the one session of chest pains.

"You're doing wonderfully," the therapist remarked. A little flicker of hope suddenly ignited in the deepest reaches of my soul. Did I dare believe I could actually regain my health? At the end of the session I stepped on the scales. Two hundred eighteen pounds. I had lost almost five pounds in my first week! For one who had always struggled so hard to lose even a few pounds, the loss was a real morale booster!

One of the basic principles of Scripture the Weimar staff holds to is the Sabbatarian principle. They believe God has made one day in seven for rest and restoration. So, the next day being the Sabbath, everything other than meals shut down, and we rested, staff and guests alike.

The start of activities the following morning marked the beginning of my second week at Weimar. I almost looked forward to getting out of bed and heading out for the morning walk. Five miles! And at a fairly brisk pace. I still took some nitroglycerin, but the ability to walk five miles and still be alive, much less feel good, was unbelievable.

That morning on the exercise bicycle I found myself pushing to see how far I could go. It was the first time in months I had felt like pushing at anything. All my ambition had long since evaporated into apathy, but now I felt faint fires of my old drive being rekindled. I pedaled eight miles!

To say I was exhilarated would be an understatement. I felt literally as if I had been born again. I was mentally alert and physically vibrant. My head was totally clear for the first time in many years! Now a genuine belief was beginning to dawn in me that I could regain my lost health after all. The despair and depression I had labored under for months was beginning to roll away. I knew God in His providential sovereignty was setting me on a new path.

I fairly talked the doctor's ears off about how good I was beginning to feel. "How did you get along without your insulin?" he finally asked.

Red-faced, I confessed, "Doctor, I'm sorry I didn't have the courage to follow your instruction totally. I only cut the dose in half."

He smiled with understanding and said, "Why not drop it altogether now? If you have trouble, we have the staff and equipment to help you out."

I stopped the insulin completely and have never had an injection since. Dropping those insulin injections was a very significant milestone in my recovery. That daily dose of insulin had been the most graphic reminder of my degenerating condition. Eliminating the injections was an exciting indication to me that I had started the road back to health.*

---

*As noted concerning my exercise program, no aspect of my treatment is necessarily applicable to others. Since discontinuing insulin injections could be dangerous, I urge readers not to do so without the advice of a physician.

4
A New Start

Improvement in my condition over the next three weeks was as steady, though not as dramatic, as the progress I had made my first week. I continued to improve my performance on the outdoor track and on the stationary bicycle, while decreasing the amount of nitroglycerin I needed to get through each session of angina.

My weight continued to drop as well. I had lost about fifteen pounds when I noticed that my pants would no longer stay up unless they were belted tightly about my shrinking waist. I took great delight in standing in our room, letting go of my pants and watching them fall uninterrupted from my waist to the floor. I don't know why that simple act was so utterly delightful, but I would repeat it three or four times in a row several times a day.

The quality of the Weimar staff impressed us more as our time at the Institute continued. Far from being wild-eyed fanatics, they are formally qualified M.D.'s and registered nurses and all the therapists are licensed in their particular fields. These deeply dedicated men and women have renounced the lucrative professional practices that were open to them and have bound themselves together in an exciting conspiracy of concern, commitment, and healing that springs from the inner spiritual commitment of each. Their deep commitment is expressed in the practice of prayer with each "guest" at the end of every session. These prayers, though simple and unpretentious, never ceased to move me.

The Weimar Institute, however, is more than a group of fine Christian people doing good works. The staff is deeply dedicated to a biblically based life-style. In deference to the secular orientation of most of their guests, they do not go around quoting Scripture chapters and verses, but rather continually refer to the stewardship of our bodies, the acknowledgement of the divine purpose of creation, and our need to trust in divine power in all of life.

The daily medical lectures were of inestimable value to me. For years I had followed doctors' instructions and popped prescribed pills of medication into my mouth with blind faith, only to find no cure at the end of the road. Weimar's approach is different. They believe that if we understand the rationale for our changes in life-style, the chances of maintaining the desired discipline are far greater.

Each morning, simply and systematically, using charts and simple chalk drawings, the highly trained medical professionals reduced their sophisticated medical concepts and terminology to layman's language. As the days went by I began to understand for the first time how the years of an improper life-style had almost destroyed my life. I could also see that a new life-style could reverse at least part of that destructive course.

Ruth was invaluable to me in these lectures. As a registered nurse, she was able to digest more fully the implications of what was taught, and later help me understand portions that had not been completely clear. She took copious notes which were to be a tremendous help as we moved into our new life-style.

Weimar's philosophy can be capsulized in their motto, "New Start." Each letter of their motto introduces a word that describes an aspect of their philosophy:

N-Nutrition
E-Exercise
W-Water

S-Sunlight
T-Temperance
A-Air
R-Rest
T-Trust in Divine Power

Their program is based on using the natural healing and maintenance elements which God has placed in our natural environment. Traditional medical philosophy, for the most part, emphasizes curing diseases with drugs and artificial substances *after* the affliction has already established a foothold. Weimar's more natural philosophy, however, emphasizes *preventing* illness by proper care of the body. *In many cases, simply embracing proper habits of health and living are sufficient to reverse the destructive path that certain ailments have already taken.* As well-trained doctors, they do not totally eschew the traditional methods of the medical profession, but simply seek to use them as a supplement to the natural healing process God has already given.

Here is a synopsis of their philosophy:

Nutrition. "N" stands for nutrition, which of course is the mainstay of the program. We are only as healthy, they taught us, as what we put into our bodies. According to a vast amount of current medical information, most of the degenerative diseases that plague modern America (heart problems, high blood pressure, certain types of cancers, stroke, blood imbalances, etc.) are primarily the result of improper diet. We eat far too much fat and sugar and too many refined, processed, artificial foods.

The foods we should be eating are, first of all, extremely low in fat. Meat, dairy products, and oils contain most of the fat we eat. (The average American, by the way, receives 40% to 50% of his daily caloric intake in some form of fat.) Ruth and I had always been heavy red meat eaters, having some form of beef at least four or five times a week. We were now told that red meat and dairy products should be almost totally eliminated from our diets. Too much fat in a diet has a number of deleterious effects. The worst effect is an increase in the fat levels of our blood (cholesterol and triglycerides) to the point that the cholesterol deposits begin clogging the arteries and restricting the blood flow until coronary heart disease or a stroke results. Beyond that, fat causes the blood to thicken, cutting down on the oxygen flow to the body. Fat also impedes proper metabolism and fosters diabetes. Finally, the excessive calories gained from eating too much fat add directly to our own fat deposits in the form of extra pounds.

Sugar is also forbidden. I was suprised to learn that

most Americans receive almost 25% of their daily caloric intake directly from sugars. That meant each of us had been eating about two pounds of sugar per week! Only about a quarter of that, however, came from using sugar directly. Most sugar comes from processed foods in the form of additives such as corn syrup, sucrose, etc. Read the labels on food products and you may be surprised, as I was, to find that almost *all* processed foods have sugars added.

Sugars, whether in the form of white refined sugar, or honey and molasses (which some people erroneously believe are healthful substitutes) do a number of things to our system. The sugar we cannot immediately metabolize is converted into blood fat, which runs around sludging up our blood stream, clings to the walls of our arteries, or is added to our fat storage as extra pounds. Excess sugar also stimulates the pancreas, a condition which, over a period of years, can lead to hypoglycemia or diabetes. If you don't think you eat a lot of sugar, just examine your food labels for awhile.

Weimar also insisted we eliminate salt from the diet as much as possible. Most Americans are salt addicts and, like sugar, salt is a standard additive in almost all processed food, even without what we use from the shaker. Salt causes water retention in the tissues, and most medical authorities feel it is a major contributor to hypertension or high blood pressure.

Caffeine is an absolute anathema to the natural way of eating. Caffeine from coffee, tea, and soft drinks has been shown to produce irregular heartbeats and to raise the level of free fatty acids in the blood (which contributes to coronary heart disease). It also raises the level of blood glucose in diabetics, increases gastric acid secretions, and produces high blood pressure. Caffeine also stimulates the production of adrenalin from the adrenal glands, which can play havoc with blood sugar levels, agitate the nervous system, and lead to fatigue and exhaustion. In addition, caffeine robs the body of many beneficial vitamins and minerals.

As a drug, caffeine is powerful enough to produce uncomfortable withdrawal symptoms when consumption ceases. One need only drink about two cups of coffee a day to feel the withdrawal effects in the form of severe headaches or nausea when he decides to give it up. Ruth and I had been heavy coffee drinkers, and now that we have given it up we are grateful for calmer nerves and more restful nights.

Alcohol, like caffeine, is also a drug to be avoided. As a first cousin to pure sugar, it raises the fat levels of the blood, as well as fogging the mind and contributing to the destruction of brain tissues by cutting down on the oxygen-carrying capacity of the blood.

"What is there left to eat?" Ruth and I wondered as we listened to the doctors' warnings. Ruth, with her background in traditional medicine, had been taught that our major source of protein should be animal protein, that is, meat or dairy products. The egg, to her, was the perfect breakfast food. But once all the standard sources of protein had been eliminated from our diet, we learned we could obtain all the needed proteins through the proper eating of *unrefined* carbohydrates, fruits and vegetables, with an occasional portion of poultry or fish if desired. As occasional dieters, we had always considered carbohydrates a dirty word. Carbohydrates meant cakes, ice cream and "nasty" starches. Now we learned that *unrefined* carbohydrates such as cereals, whole grains, beans, peas, vegetables, and fruits offered a wonderfully adequate assortment of protein and amino acids without all the undesirable fat and sugar.

Unrefined carbohydrates were endorsed as opposed to milled and processed flours and grains. It is common knowledge that the milling process removes much of the nutritional value of the food as well as valuable fiber, essential for maintaining regular bowel activity and preventing diseases of the colon. Colon-rectal cancers, by the way, are among the leading causes of cancer death in this country today. Many medical authorities feel that these forms of cancer are largely due to a lack of adequate fiber in our diet.

The complete explanation of the Weimar philosophy of diet is well beyond the scope of this book or my ability to relate. A bibliography has been added for those who want further information. I would only add that Ruth, whose medical training ran almost contrary to the Weimar approach, was totally converted by the dual witness of the dramatic change in our own lives and the soundness of Weimar's medical logic and documentation. Their sources, by the way, were numerous credible authorities in the medical profession, and their dedicated approach to nutrition is being increasingly espoused in many circles of health care.

As mentioned earlier, the objective of the nutritional program for me was to reduce the levels of fat in my blood, which were having two deadly effects on my system. First, years of high fat and cholesterol levels had left the arteries of my heart clogged with fatty plaque which was restricting the vital flow of blood and oxygen to my heart muscles. Second, my blood stream itself was so clogged with fat that its essential oxygen-carrying capability was severely impaired, further reducing the flow of oxygen to my heart muscles. Reducing the fat levels in my blood would partially restore the oxygen-carrying ability and help the efficiency of what circulation I had, and the reduction of blood fats would reduce at least some of the fat buildup in my arteries. Not too much plaque reduction could be predicted, due to my advanced condition and subsequent hardening of the plaque.

The reduction of the fat level and regulation of the sugar intake inherent in the diet were also responsible for the disappearance of my diabetes.

The type of diet we were now following also resulted in a substantial overall reduction in our daily caloric intake. The resulting weight loss not only greatly increased my general sense of well-being, but also alleviated a significant amount of the labor required of my already weakened heart. While we experienced other benefits from this new and disciplined way of eating, the improvement in my heart and circulatory system was the most dramatic.

Exercise. The second letter of their motto is "E" for exercise. Exercise is a major ally of nutrition. The primary exercise promoted by Weimar is walking. Of course, running and jogging have excellent benefits as well, but the large number of minor injuries experienced by many joggers incline these doctors to the more benign form of exercise.

Exercise has many desirable benefits. First, it generally increases the flow of blood and oxygen to all the body, but specifically to the heart. Daily exercise of the heart increases its stamina and condition and also helps develop alternate circulation paths for the blood around its clogged arteries. Additionally, exercise helps lower the level of blood fat and sets the metabolism at a somewhat higher rate, thus burning off excess calories and helping in weight control.

Today, Ruth and I find our most useful form of exercise is fast walking. We try to walk morning and evening, approximately two miles each time. Sometimes this is difficult in our extensive travels; however, we usually manage to measure out the proper distance and walk it. In foreign countries and strange cities this has afforded some interesting exposures to different cultures, language problems (trying to get directions when we're lost), and bits of scenery both pleasant and otherwise which we might normally have missed. I also play racquetball fairly regularly, and in the United States and Canada I find facilities quite available. We have an exercise bicycle which, although we do not use regularly, comes in very handy on days when the weather is too severe for us to go outdoors.

Water. The third letter is "W" for water. Quite a change! Our doctors suggested we drink at least eight to ten glasses of water between meals to aid in the purging of the system. We do not drink water thirty minutes before or one hour after meals in order to prevent dilution of stomach acids, which would hinder in proper digestion.

Even before we went to Weimar, Ruth was quite committed to drinking water as a form of health care. Weimar only served to support her contentions and leave me without any excuse. When we are home, I am presented first thing in the morning with a large glassful of water. During the rest of the day I can expect to confront full glasses of water placed at strategic points around the house. Often the operation is more direct, and Ruth will walk into my study with the glass in her hand. Sometimes I react and say, "Set it down!" and try to ignore it. But it isn't long until I give in and drink it. Otherwise, it insists on sitting there and challenging me! When we are traveling it is sometimes more difficult to maintain a regimen of water intake, and my body registers its complaints in various obvious ways.

Sunlight. The fourth letter is "S" for sunlight. I was constantly confronted at Weimar with the emphasis on all the available natural means of therapy and health maintenance: water, air, exercise, sunshine. These seem too ordinary for many modern sophisticated minds who have come to prefer unreadable drug prescriptions which must, by the very fact that they are written in Latin, contain some magic formula for recovery. I had always thought of sunlight only as something preferable to rain and the source of a summertime tan. However, by the time I got through listening to my mentors at Weimar, I realized that the sun offered far greater benefits for me personally. Dr. Zane R. Kime, who was closely associated with Weimar while I was there, has written a book entitled *Sunlight Could Save Your Life.* The contents of the book provide a compelling case for the powerful therapeutic benefit of sunlight.

Again, this presents some problem to Ruth and me as we travel a great deal. While living in California we were richly blessed by being able to get sun almost daily year round. And again, I have to say that I always felt better for it, and when forced by travel to be in climates where sunshine is not available, I feel I am missing a proven source of health and therapy for myself. Since moving from California I miss my daily sunbaths more than I thought possible.

Temperance. The fifth letter is "T" for temperance. Temperance is quite often associated almost exclusively with alcohol consumption. Its broad definition, however, is "self-restraint in conduct, expression, indulgence of the appetites, etc." Temperance in the Bible is one of the fruits of the Spirit and should characterize the life of a committed Christian. In another place it is referred to as a part of the maturation process, which must be cultivated if one would "grow up into Christ in all things."

I find, in common with many Christians, the tendency to have my own catalog of sins. This probably comes from a particular religious background where certain things were emphasized as being wrong. These received major attention while equally important things were neglected because they were not emphasized in my particular religious milieu. For example, it is not uncommon to hear some grossly overweight preacher inveigh other sinful indulgences while totally unaware that the visible evidence of his own intemperance virtually nullifies his credibility. Any lack of restraint is an evidence of intemperance and in the context of Scripture is both grievous to the Holy Spirit and an evidence of our immaturity.

Weimar brought this quite vividly to my attention. I realized I had been intemperate in eating and drinking, and in other areas as well. Not only was the teaching on temperance convicting, but the behavior of the staff as they manifested temperance in so many ways served to make me painfully aware of my bulging tummy as well as other indulgences not so evident. It is possible to be quite mature in some areas and very immature in others. For me, the bathroom scales have now become one important way in which I monitor my spirituality and maturity.

Air. "A" in the "New Start" motto stands for air and signifies Weimar's concern that we receive sufficient oxygen for achieving and maintaining health. Lack of oxygen is believed to be a factor in most degenerative diseases such as arteriosclerosis (hardening of the arteries), arthritis, hypertension, diabetes, cataracts, and cancer. We were shown how a more adequate supply of oxygen can bring a decrease in blood cholesterol and triglycerides, which helps unclog arteries and blood vessels, thus increasing healthy blood flow.

Moreover, we learned that air is ionized with both negatively-charged oxygen molecules and positively-charged carbon dioxide molecules. Clean fresh air with high negative ion content is able to purify, destroy, or render inactive bacteria and viruses as well as other harmful substances.

We were suprised to learn that the average person is a very shallow breather, normally using only 30 to 40% of his lung capacity. Obviously then, the more pure, outdoor air we breath, the better off we are.

Rest. "R" stands for the principle of rest. In many ways Weimar was a time of reckoning for me. I realized that I had abused my body in many ways through the years. Some of these abuses could be traced directly to negligence and indulgence while others had come from a fierce dedication to misguided commitments. Lack of adequate rest falls into the latter category. Early in my ministry, I decided that sleep was a great enemy of spiritual progress. I would deliberately test my body to see how long I could go without rest so as to provide more time for study and preparation for my service to God. This bad habit eventually resulted in a chronically irregular sleep pattern, which undoubtedly contributed much to my ultimate breakdown. As I listened to the Weimar staff stress the need for rest I realized I had probably sinned here as much as anywhere. But I am thankful to God that I am much better now and my current rest habits are more consistent with healthful living. I am aware, however, that longstanding habits still lurk in the background, and I diligently guard myself against slipping into them again.

The subject of rest, of course, looms large in the Scriptures. God Himself not only rested on the seventh day; He incorporated rest into the very fabric of His commandments to man: "Six days shall you labor and do all your work, but the seventh day is a sabbath of the Lord your God. In it you shall not do any work..." (Ex. 20:10).

Trust. The final "T" stands for trust in divine power. Of course, *everything* Weimar did grew out of their conviction that life can have no mental or physical health apart from a foundation of faith in Almighty God. I had entered Weimar functioning at a low percentage of normal potential. But by the time Ruth and I left I was an altogether different person. My weight had dropped from two hundred twenty-three pounds to just above two hundred pounds. My blood pressure was normal for the first time in many years. The cholesterol and triglycerides in my blood were approaching a safe level. I was walking around five miles a day at a brisk pace and riding between five and six miles on the stationary bicycle. I felt alive and alert. Depression and despair had been replaced by hope and anticipation. With the exception of occasional nitroglycerin for the residual angina which now plagued me only during vigorous exercise, I was off all medication.

God, in His providence, had chosen to use the Institute to do for me what nothing else up until that time had done. I could not pretend to understand the mysterious ways of His providential dealings. I still believe as strongly as ever in God's power and willingness to heal His people supernaturally, but as we prepared to leave Weimar, I could only bow in worshipful adoration before the One whose great care and infinite longsuffering bore with this unworthy servant for so long.

On the trip back to San Diego, I felt as if I had just received reprieve from a death sentence, and that a few years at least might now be added to my journey. I deeply sensed the Lord was restoring not only my health, but also some understanding of how He expected me to steward the physical body of my earthly sojourning.

Back in my study at home, I set out to discover what God's Word would reveal concerning His attitude toward my physical body.

5
An Unhealthy Emphasis

Having God roll back new horizons of His Word has always been a thrilling adventure for me. As I began to pursue the scriptural precepts about caring for our physical bodies, I found myself at once convicted and excited. A new vision of the totality of God's majestic purpose for all His creation began to burst on my consciousness. I was convicted because I saw how sorely I had transgressed the sacred trust He had allotted me in my physical body, and I was excited because I caught a glimpse of new and wonderful avenues of dominion opening for God's people.

Actually, my study of this subject had begun earlier, during the weeks preceding our trip to Weimar. Those were some of the most discouraging days I have ever known in my life. My deep depression was effected in large measure, I am sure, by my physical discomforts, but perhaps more than anything else by the fact that for the first time in my life I could see absolutely no future for myself. My life seemed to be ignobly whimpering to a close. I was no longer looking for God to heal me.

While I did not lack faith in either His ability or His desire for me to be whole, I seemed to know deep in my spirit that a supernatural restoration of my physical health was just not in God's purposes for me at that time.

Those depressing days, however, were opportune for some needed introspection and reflection. Could this debilitating illness be God's highest purpose for my life? I could not see how.

I remembered my years of travel with William Branham's miracle healing ministry. I had watched thousands of people pressing forward to receive the healing of their bodies. As I watched this unending stream of afflicted humanity, it was obvious many of the people coming for healing were quite evidently the victims of their own self-mistreatment. Many were suffering from diseases and ailments relating to excessive weight, smoking, or the abuse of alcohol. I remembered at the time wondering what the divine attitude toward miraculous healing would be when the sickness in question is obviously self-inflicted by failure to care for the body in a proper manner. I had even wondered if this overt neglect was the reason many were not dramatically healed in those crusades. Could it be that God had ordained a different path to healing for them?

Traditionally, evangelical Christian thought had given little emphasis to the care of the human body. As an evangelical, I never considered my physical body in the context of my Christian discipleship and submission to the Word of God.

Not only am I an evangelical—I am an "evangelistic" evangelical. So strong was my burden for evangelism that with the congregation's support, I renamed the church I had pastored for over twenty years "The Evangelistic Tabernacle." The name reflected my deep and passionate dedication to evangelism and my pastoral desire to lead my people into the same fervor.

I was burdened with "saving souls." I still am. But as evangelicals our emphasis on the regeneration of the soul had left the status of the body undefined in the salvation process. The evangelistic approach preaches the soul into repentance and the new birth, makes sure it is filled with the Holy Spirit, rigorously teaches it the dogmas of Christian theology, disciplines it with biblical morality, blesses it with music and wonderful preaching—but in the process leaves the poor body behind as a struggling pilgrim. About the only teaching we ever received on the body was how it related to the soul in a narrow range of ethical matters—that is, make sure your soul does not let your body fornicate, get drunk, or indulge in gluttony. In short, most evangelical teaching does not accurately reflect the proper emphasis on the physical body that we find in the Bible. Is there a reason for this? I think so.

Our view of the body—as well as much of life—has been more extensively molded by Greek philosophy than most of us could ever fully realize. Some may wonder why this influence is a problem: After all, the Greeks were not so bad—they gave us democracy, the Olympics, and some pretty good literature. But the problem is not what we inherited from the Greeks *in particular*; the problem is a general way of looking at life and the world which we call "humanism." The Greeks saw man as the ultimate measure of all things. There was no source of knowledge or authority above man himself.

The primary source of this philosophy was Plato. Plato taught that the soul was superior and the body inferior. His influence left the Greeks with the idea that you could do whatever you wanted with your body as long as you took good care of your mind and your soul.

The outcome of the Greek humanistic thinking became evident by the New Testament period. We catch a glimpse of its effects on the non-Jewish world through the epistles of the apostle Paul.

The Greek view of the body was particularly addressed in Paul's first letter to the Corinthians. G. Campbell Morgan once commented that error in doctrine or conduct which the scripture sought to correct in a church was inevitably a reflection of the prevailing culture of the particular city in which that church was located. Instead of the church changing the city, the city was influencing the church. The culture of Corinth was Hellenistic, and the Greek view of the body had infested the Corinthian church.

Corinth was the political capital of Greece and the seat of its commerical and intellectual life. Its strategic location gave it wide influence. Among other things it was noted for its licentiousness. The sacred temple of Venus, the goddess of love, located in Corinth was endowed with a thousand priestesses whose service to their deity included prostitution with male worshipers. The licentious life of Corinth became so notorious that the Greeks developed a special verb to describe it: "to Corinthianize," which meant "to play the wanton." It is also significant that the terrible indictment of degenerate culture recorded in the first chapter of Romans was written while Paul was staying in Corinth (see Rom. 1:18-28).

59

To the Greeks and Romans, food and sex were considered as undifferentiated appetites to be appeased. It is therefore not surprising that the Corinthians would carry this attitude over into their profession of Christianity. As Paul was addressing these attitudes in his Corinthian correspondence, we find some positive teaching in 1 Corinthians chapters six and seven on the divine estimate of the Christian's body. As I began to understand the Corinthians' view of our physical body, I finally began to see why many of them struggled with believing in the physical resurrection from the dead. They could easily believe in an afterlife existence in some mystical, spiritual form. But to believe that the physical body with all its licentiousness, was worthy of redemption and glorification ran contrary to all their Greek culture. The glorious fifteenth chapter of 1 Corinthians on resurrection was written to correct a cultural problem as much as a theological one!

Though the New Testament church was successful in eradicating many of the moral errors that grew from the Greeks' humanistic view of the body, much of the basic influence of the Greek view of the body continues to this present day. We are all too inclined to view our physical bodies as shackles which fetter the noble spirit and prevent it from being free to experience higher realms of existence. By embracing this philosophy, however, we find ourselves cut off from vast portions of our rightful salvation.

Jesus stated that "salvation is from the Jews" (Jn. 4:22). I believe this refers to more than the Jews as the national people through which the Messiah, the Savior of the world, was born. The Jews also brought us a God-given life-style and world view designed to lead us out of satanic, self-centered humanism. As the people of God, we are the continuance of God's speaking through Abraham, Isaac, and Jacob. As Christians our roots are in the Hebrew scriptures and not in Greek philosophy. Therefore it is not legitimate for us as God's people to draw our view of the world and our existence in it from the philosophy of a pagan culture; rather, we must draw the totality of our world view and life-style from the Hebrew culture which was God-ordained and patterned from its very inception.

Regarding the human body, we find that the Hebrews viewed the body as a part of the whole man. Their physical bodies were so integrated into the totality of their beings that their vocabulary never developed a distinct word to describe their bodies. The Hebrew did not "have a body" because his body was so much a part of himself. About eighty times in the Old Testament the body is referred to by means of one of its individual members—that is, the heart, the belly, the inward parts, etc. To the Hebrews the physical body was a perfectly valid manifestation of the soul. They saw no separation or distinction. Indeed the body was the outward form of the soul. The Hebrews, therefore, quite logically believed the body was as important in the eyes of God as was the soul. Tragically, however, most of us are still operating out of a Greek mind-set rather than a Hebrew mind-set. And as a result, we have neglected, despised, over-indulged our physical bodies, and in the process relegated them to a place of inferiority in the kingdom of God.

There is one scripture which, as it appears in the King James Version, seems to support the Greek attitude to the body. In Philippians 3:21, the body is referred to as "vile." But when that scripture speaks of "the body of our humiliation" (a closer translation), it is not implying that the body is inferior to the soul or that there is anything inherently evil and demeaning about the physical state. The only problem with our "humble bodies" is that they are time-space bodies designed for time-space living. Presently, the life of our bodies is in the blood, but one day these same bodies will be animated by the spirit when we are caught up in the resurrection and begin to live in the eternal realm.

Allow me to illustrate. Like many of you, I have been in meetings where God's Spirit was moving in a particularly powerful manner. During such times, I have actually felt I could almost step off into the air and begin to fly. Such experiences come when the eternal Spirit, who raised Christ and will one day animate our mortal bodies, tries to express Himself through this time-space body. The problem is that a time-space body cannot adequately respond to the movings of the eternal Spirit. When we find ourselves in a wonderful spiritual plane, we clap, praise, dance, shout and try to fly! But the body won't take off—it is earthbound. The physical body is temporarily "humiliating" our high destiny as children of God.

God does not consider our bodies "vile" and we must not, either. Indeed, Paul reminds us our bodies are temples of the Holy Spirit (1 Cor. 6:19-20). God has quite specifically included the body in His revealed redemptive purpose. This is made quite clear in the numerous biblical references to God's healing grace for the body. Also, scripturally my body is seen as an instrument of righteous behavior and an integral part of my being, which shares in my transformation and renewal (Rom. 12:1-2). Ultimately it is destined through resurrection to resemble the body of our risen Lord.

The negative humanistic approach which we have taken toward our bodies has led to neglect, over-indulgence, self-gratification, and other attitudes which ultimately detract from God's purposes for us. We used to have a saying when I was young in the ministry: "It is better to burn out than to rust out." Such platitudes, however, are merely pious-sounding excuses to sanctify our wanton abuse of our physical bodies.

During the time that I was traveling extensively with William Branham, I would often spend six days a week working long hours in the Branham crusades and then go home to my church on Sunday to face a full schedule. I would maintain this suicidal schedule for weeks at a time. I remember quite vividly one day slumping into a chair with my head spinning from fatigue and exhaustion, and commenting to my wife, "I know I will pay for this some day." Little did I know how dearly!

A number of years ago our Evangelistic Tabernacle had a guest speaker who ministered with a tremendous anointing and brought great blessing to our people. But he was also grossly overweight—so much so that we needed to provide two chairs for him to be able to sit comfortably in any situation. Many close friends and confidants urged him to do something about his weight, and to alter his voracious eating habits. But tragically, he reflected a common ministerial attitude; he was concerned only about "the things of the Lord."

A few years later, while still ministering in great power and anointing, he died suddenly of ailments related to his excessive obesity. The oil of the Holy Spirit's anointing that had flowed so richly through him was prematurely lost to the body of Christ because he had not cared for the vessel which carried the anointing. The anointing is a wonderful thing, but if the vessel which carries it breaks down, the ministry of grace is lost to all. He died just when he should have been entering the prime of his life and ministry, a tragic loss to the people and purposes of God.

The scripture states rather bluntly, "The dead praise not God..." (Ps. 115:17). It makes no difference whether we are brilliant, gifted, trained and anointed—we are of no use to God on earth if we are dead. There is a tremendous difference between the Lord giving one of His servants an early retirement and that servant committing suicide via neglect and disobedience. An unhealthy emphasis on the inferiority of the body is still far too widespread, and is still proving a significant hindrance to the purposes of God which demand and deserve our highest and healthiest physical response.

6
Positive Teaching on the Body

In the weeks after my stay at Weimar, I studied the Scripture systematically in order to understand the biblical principles with regard to our bodies. I would like to set forth what I found in a simple, straightforward fashion without excessive commentary. God's Word will have its own impact. In my search for His truth I found eleven basic but profound themes which I believe capture the extent and importance of the subject in the mind of the Holy Spirit.

Principle 1: My body is "for the Lord, and the Lord for the body."

"Food for the stomach and the stomach for food"—but God will destroy them both. The body is not meant for sexual immorality, but for the Lord, and the Lord for the body (1 Cor. 6:13 NIV).

Scripture makes it plain that Jesus Christ is Lord of my body. My body was designed to manifest the purposes of God, and my soul and spirit are dependent upon the body to bring worship and obedience to God. Through the fall of man the body shared the effects of alienation from God and His creational design. In redemption, however, the body as well as the soul and spirit is to be restored as an instrument to express God's holiness and righteousness. We may only want our souls saved, but God wants to save the whole "us."

We must know what the Lord requires of us with regard to our bodies, and be as obedient to those requirements as we are in other areas of our personal response to Christ's lordship. Not only do we have "a body from the Lord"—that is, His lordship over our bodies; we also find that "the Lord is for the body"— that is, the Lord is infinitely interested in the well-being and redemption of our physical bodies. My body is not a despised appendage to my soul. It has its own distinctive purpose, function, and destiny under Christ's redemptive lordship.

Principle 2: My body will be resurrected.

> By His power God raised the Lord from the dead, and he will raise us also (1 Cor. 6:14 NIV).

As Christians, our attitude toward our bodies should be significantly affected by our coming resurrection. The future resurrection of this earthly body, which will be in the same form as Christ's glorified body, should impress us with reverent concern as to how we view and trust the organ which will house our glorified personality.

Some in the Corinthian church believed that "there is

no resurrection" (1 Cor. 15:12). The Corinthians believed in life after death, but not bodily life. To them the body was more a temporary and degenerating prison house that would be happily dispensed with at death. Such an attitude naturally had a profound effect on how they treated the physical body.

Over against this degrading philosophy, Paul asserts the permanence of the body in the purposes of God through resurrection: "He will transfigure the body belonging to our humble state, and give it a form like that of His own resplendent body, by the very power which enables Him to make all things subject to Himself" (Phil. 3:21 NEB). The apostle John says as well: "What we shall be has not yet been disclosed, but we know that when it is disclosed we shall be like Him. . . . Everyone who has at heart a hope like that keeps himself pure, for he knows how pure Christ is" (1 Jn. 3:2-3 JBP). In the light of this, our whole being, including our body, should be treated in accord with its thrilling destiny.

Principle 3: My body shares the judgment.

> For we must all appear before the judgment seat of Christ, that each one may receive what is due him for the things done while in the body whether good or bad (2 Cor. 5:10 NIV).

The body is an essential part of the human personality. By means of my body I do deeds, and my body shares the "reward" of those deeds whether they are "good" or "bad." In the horrible but accurate picture of ungodly society penned by Paul in Romans, we see the body as the instrument of man's unrestrained desire for forbidden pleasure. Because they chose this course, "God gave them up to be the playthings of their own foul desires in dishonoring their own bodies" (Rom. 1:24 JBP). God's action resulted in the heathen receiving "in themselves the due penalty for their perversion" (Rom. 1:27 NIV).

The Bible pictures judgment as both present and future. "The wrath of God is being revealed from heaven against all the godlessness and wickedness of men" (Rom. 1:18 NIV), and "He has set a day when He will judge the world with justice" (Acts 17:31 NIV).

The body, as part of the total human personality, experiences its share of rewards and penalties now, and will do so at the judgment seat of Christ.

Principle 4: My body is a member of Christ.

> Do you not know that your bodies are members of Christ? (1 Cor. 6:15 NAS)

How supremely superior is the revelation of God concerning the human body, when compared with the philosophical fumblings of men in their lostness. We should be concerned and interested to discover the degree to which our Christian attitudes are still conditioned by non-biblical viewpoints. I personally recall the measure of amazement I registered when I first faced the astounding implications of the phrase—"your bodies are members of Christ!" At that time I was quite convinced that I was spiritually joined to Christ, but I had not thought of my body as sharing in that unity, at least not to the same degree. "You mean," I asked, "this dirty old

68

body I pop Rolaids into and stick under showers is part of Christ?'' My attitude probably betrayed some sub-Christian thinking on my part concerning the nature of the Christian's body.

Verse 17 in the sixth chapter of Paul's letter goes on to state that ''he that is joined unto the Lord is one with Him in spirit.'' This provides a kind of Bible logic for verse 15. If my spirit is one spirit with the Lord, and my body is ''for the Lord'' and the instrument for my spirit's manifestation, my body evidently shares that vital union. This being the case, our unity with Christ imposes the highest conceivable obligation to act consistently with this intimate and exalting relationship.

Principle 5: My body is a temple of the Holy Spirit.

Do you not know that your body is a temple of the Holy Spirit, who is in you, whom you have received from God? (1 Cor. 6:19 NIV)

We have already pointed out that the Corinthians undoubtedly were influenced by the philosophy of the Greek culture that characterized the city. This influence led to low views of the body resulting in unchristian physical behavior. Gluttony and even drunkenness were to be seen on the occasion of the Lord's Supper.

In chapter five of 1 Corinthians, the sensual violation was sexual, one notorious case of incest being cited (v. 1). Paul required that discipline be promptly and thoroughly administered. He also, however, refreshed their minds with positive teaching on the divine purpose for the body: ''Our physical body was not made for

69

sexual promiscuity, but for the Lord" (v. 13 JBP). The body is a "member of Christ" (v. 15).

Paul's teaching on the Christian character of the body could hardly have been new to the Corinthians—it is difficult to believe that in his previous personal ministry to them, Paul had not taught the Corinthians that their bodies were the temples of the Holy Spirit. But either they had conveniently forgotten Paul's doctrine, somehow subtly skirted around it, or more probably were simply disobedient. The last seems to be the case (see 2 Cor. 12:21).

In the light of their behavior they had to be reminded. "Have you forgotten," he says, "that your body is the temple of the Holy Spirit, who lives in you?" (1 Cor. 6:19 JBP). In Old Testament times the temple was "the holy place," the place of God's presence among men. Jesus, speaking of His body as "this temple," compared it with the temple in Jerusalem which He called "My Father's house" (Jn. 2:16, 19). Then Paul in this same letter to the Corinthians refers to the Church as "the temple of God" (3:16), as he does elsewhere in his writings (2 Cor. 6:16; Eph. 2:21).

How sobering and sanctifying this word should be. As the temple of God, my body stands in relationship with the glorious temple of the Old Covenant, the divinely prepared body of my incomparable Lord Jesus, and the ultimate community of God's presence and purpose. This one fact would seem to be sufficient to secure an attitude of holy, healthy concern for the manner in which I care for my body. But there is more.

Principle 6: My body is God's purchased possession.

You are not your own; you were bought at a price. Therefore honor God with your body (1 Cor. 6:19-20 NIV).

We hear much in our permissive and humanist-dominated society about people having the right to do with their bodies what they will. This attitude is an understandable one for people who are "lost." Such foolishness is totally unacceptable, however, for those who have been "found."

If a Christian has been well-instructed in the most elementary facts of his salvation, he should know he has been "redeemed." I have been purchased—I am the property of my Redeemer. Every part of me belongs to Him by purchase. I do not have independent rights to my body, or any other part of my being: I am *all* His! Paul bluntly says, "Ye are not your own," and remember, on this occasion he is speaking of our bodies. There is not a single Christian who has an independent, unilateral right to his body.

Paul is not content just to mention the purchase; he wants us to remember the "price." "At what a price!" is the way J.B. Phillips translates it. The emphasis is well taken. We are told that God purchased us "with His own blood" (Acts 20:28), and we are His "purchased possession" (Eph. 1:14).

"Therefore bring glory to God in your body" (1 Cor. 6:20 JBP).

Principle 7: My body is my "home."

If the earthly tent we live in is destroyed, we have a building from God, an eternal house in heaven, not

71

built by human hands. . . . Therefore we are always confident and know that as long as we are at home in the body we are away from the Lord (2 Cor. 5:1, 6 NIV).

My body is my "earthly house." In this passage my present physical home stands in contrast with my "house which is from Heaven" (v. 1, 6). We do not want to concern ourselves at this point with Paul's teaching on my "house from heaven," but simply with the biblical reference to my body as my house or home.

To the biblical Christian who truly grasps the fullness of his redemption, it becomes immediately obvious that while my body is my home, I do not own it. Instead, I occupy my bodily home by the kindness of a wealthy Benefactor who came along when my house was owned and run by a vicious landlord. He bought my house and turned it over to me, asking me to care for it in accord with His requirements. Interestingly, His requirements for the care of my house are lovingly designed to ensure my peace, joy, and security. The kindness of my Benefactor and a proper concern for my own highest good should combine to make me want to be a good householder.

Principle 8: My body is a sacrificial offering to God.

Therefore, I urge you, brothers, in view of God's mercy, to offer your bodies as living sacrifices, holy and pleasing to God (Rom. 12:1 NIV).

Reading this verse, we immediately think of the Old

Testament sacrifices. The book of Leviticus, which deals with various divinely required sacrifices, commences by giving specific directions concerning the body of the sacrificial animal. The sacrifice must be without blemish (Lev. 1:3), and after being slain its inner parts and legs were washed in the water (Lev. 1:9). When offered, the sacrifice was to be "a sweet savor unto the Lord" (v. 9).

Paul uses the language of sacrificial ritual to give a special significance to the appeal he makes for the presentation of our bodies to God. As the devout Israelite presented his lamb as an offering to his Lord, so we are to offer our bodies. But there is a difference. The Israelite's lamb was to be slain. We, however, "present ourselves to God as those alive from the dead" (Rom. 6:13 NAS).

We are a sacrifice that lives. Christ's sacrificial death enables us to live a sacrificial life. We live to become, at every moment of our existence, the active agent of the divine will. Please note that Paul does not ask his readers to present their "souls and spirits" as a sacrifice. As a good Jew, he believed that if the body was presented, the soul and spirit had to come along.

Our "living sacrifice" is to be holy. This undoubtedly means "without blemish," or free from those defects which would cause an offering to be rejected. It is also to be acceptable, which would point to the Old Testament when it speaks of the offering as a sweet-smelling savor.

The presentation of our bodies to God as a living, constant sacrifice of our members to His will is our "reasonable service" or "an act of intelligent worship" (JBP). Such a sacrifice is the most sound, sane, intelligent, reasonable, and rational thing a redeemed creature can do!

Beyond being our reasonable service to the Lord, our sacrifice is also the wisest move we can make. When we give our bodies to the Lord we enter into a kind of divine contract or covenant. The Lord would state something like this: "You give me your body, and I—the Creator, the Redeemer, and the God of the Universe—will keep you in the knowledge of My will from this day until time ends for you." There is also a maintenance clause in the contract: If we give Him our bodies in covenant, He will keep them quickened and patched up until the resurrection. Who could walk away from that deal?

Principle 9: My body is an armory for righteousness.

> Do not, then, allow sin to establish any power over your mortal bodies in making you give way to your lusts, nor hand over your organs to be, as it were, weapons of evil for the devil's purposes. But like men rescued from certain death, put yourselves in God's hands as weapons of good for His own purposes (Rom 6:12-13 JBP).

Sin, in this passage, is referred to as a king who had previously ruled over my body, requiring me to be subject to its appetites. This destructive sovereign had enlisted the various parts of my body as weapons in the service of unrighteousness, with death as the wages for my service (Rom. 6:3). Our Lord Jesus Christ changed that. He dethroned the king, delivered me from sin's army, and enlisted the various parts of my body to be used as weapons of righteousness. So Paul exhorts us to put ourselves at the disposal of God, as dead men raised to life. My body is a weapon to be used on the side of righteousness. It follows, then, that I ought to give my body the kind of care and treatment that will enable it to be most effective in its prescribed role in the warfare.

Principle 10: My body is to be that of a well-conditioned athlete.

> I buffet my body and make it my slave, lest possibly, after I have preached to others, I myself should be disqualified (1 Cor. 9:27 NAS).

The Corinthians would have no problem understanding Paul's reference to athletic contests. Every sizable Greek city had its gymnasium and stadium or race course. The Olympic athletic games between the Greek city-states were conducted biannually near Corinth, with visitors from all parts of the empire in attendance. So when Paul chose for his illustrations two of the sports, racing and boxing, the Corinthians could hardly miss the point.

The same two sports he refers to here, he later uses to describe his life and service for the Lord: "I have fought a good fight (boxing), I have finished my course (racing)" (2 Tim. 4:7).

It becomes obvious to us when reading the first Corinthian letter that the Corinthians lacked discipline in every area of life. In the ninth chapter, borrowing a figure from the athletic contest, Paul likens the Christian life to a race and boxing match. In connection with a race, he urges, "So run that ye may obtain." A competitor must have a desire to win. Desire alone, however, will not suffice. The athlete must train to be in top physical form: "Every competitor in athletic events goes into serious training" (1 Cor. 9:25 JBP). "Let us strip off everything that hinders us," says another Bible writer, "as well as the sin which dogs our feet, and let us run the race that we have to run with patience, our eyes fixed on Jesus, the source and the goal of our faith" (Heb. 12:1-2 JBP).

Paul was apparently impressed by the kind of dedication and discipline that characterized these athletes. "Athletes," he said, "will take tremendous pains for a fading crown of leaves." What, then, should be the Christian's commitment, since "our contest is for an eternal crown that will never fade"? (1 Cor. 9:25 JBP)

Challenged by the lesser to excel at the greater, Paul says, "I run the race, then, with determination" (v. 26 JBP). Then moving from running to boxing he becomes very specific about the place of his body in the greater spiritual contest. "I am no shadow-boxer," he writes. "I really fight!" (v. 26 JBP). And then his application takes a unique turn as he treats his body as an opponent: "I bruise my own body and make it know its master" (v. 27 NEB). This is strong language. The word translated "bruise" means "to hit under the eye"—that is, to buffet or disable an antagonist as a pugilist.

Paul realized that if he was to fulfill his work for God, *he must be master of his body*. If an athlete could master his body for fleeting glory and a perishable crown, how much more should the Christian take authority over the illegitimate and excessive sensual desires of his body! With Paul this was not optional. His body was his only means of serving God. To fail to keep his body under the control of his God-mastered spirit was to risk being "disqualified."

> **Principle 11: My body is something I "nourish and cherish"** (Lev. 19:18; Mt. 19:19; 22:39; Rom. 13:9; Gal. 5:14; Jas. 2:8; Eph. 5:28-29; 2 Tim. 3:2). No man ever yet hated his own flesh (Eph. 5:29).

The importance of caring for our bodies is indirectly referred to in Paul's teaching on the marriage relationship. Men are to "love their wives as their own bodies." God's order for marriage is that the "two shall become one flesh." Therefore, stating the husband's responsibility as "head of the wife," He commands the husband to love his wife as his own body since the two are "one flesh." He then points up a generally accepted fact: "No man ever yet hated his own flesh; but nourishes and cherishes it."

The Bible disapproves of men who are "self-lovers" (2 Tim. 3:2). Is the alternative to hate ourselves? Hardly. Obviously we are looking at different views of love, or a "double self-love." Of the man who loves himself in the bad sense, it is also said that he is a "pleasure-lover more than a God-lover" (2 Tim. 3:4). The self-love referred to here is self-indulgence. If to love is to "choose the highest well-being of someone," then a self-lover fails miserably. In indulging himself he neglects God and others, and so disregards essential parts of a normal life context.

With a proper desire for the highest well-being of our physical body, we will intelligently nourish and cherish it, or as Bishop Moule comments, we will "develop its good condition and study its well-being, its healthful comfort." *Nourish* refers to "the strengthening by food, renewing the life," and *cherish* to the "protection and preservation of life."

We can only conclude that it is not only man's instinct but his duty to protect and nourish that mysterious work of God, his body, connected as it is by God's will in a thousand ways to the action of his spirit.

7
Divine Healing

My emphasis to this point has been on the Christian's responsibility to give proper care to his or her physical body. Such emphasis has been deliberate in light of my own experience and the pronounced *lack* of emphasis physical stewardship has received in most Christian circles. In no way, however, do I wish to leave the impression that I do not believe in God's intervention to heal the sick. I believe in supernatural healing based on the Scriptures. I have personally experienced its blessing and have prayed for others as they have received that grace.

The need to emphasize our part in caring for our bodies originates from a lack of sufficient balance in the past. To find a scriptural balance we need to see physical stewardship and divine healing as two sides of the same coin, or as separate aspects of the same covenant.

All divine healing is based on the Covenant. In the Covenant our bodies become the property of the Lord Jesus Christ, and He is responsible for repairs. We are responsible to call His attention to the breakdowns. If you happen to rent a house from a good landlord, you know he never minds keeping the place up. If the roof leaks or the plumbing breaks down, you call him and he sends someone over to fix the problem at his expense, since he is the owner. Once I surrender my body to the Lord as a temple for His Spirit, as the new Landlord He becomes responsible for repairs. As a member of the Covenant, I now have the privilege to call Him when my body breaks down. "Lord, your house needs some repairs...." Often He responds very graciously and sends some repairmen around to fix the place up.

If, however, I am constantly calling the landlord for repairs because I have been throwing chairs through the windows and flushing diapers down the toilet then eventually he's either going to charge me for the repairs, or let me live in the mess I've made, or tell me to get out. That's what my body's Landlord did to me. As a matter of fact, I came very close to being evicted!

As I understand our Covenant, the Lord will take care of the normal repairs, but we are responsible to honor Him by keeping His house in the best possible shape we can. Sometimes in His grace He will effect some repair even when we haven't done our part. But if we are wise, we will never presume on God's grace.

Scripturally, the reciprocal responsibility within the Covenant is expressed in a passage that contains one of the most quoted verses concerning divine healing in all the Bible, Exodus 15:26: "I am the Lord that healeth thee." Unfortunately, this proclamation is often blindly affirmed as an unconditional fact, with the unwarranted assumption that whenever there is sickness there should be automatic healing, since the Lord has declared Himself to be our Healer.

However, when quoted in its proper context, this much misused verse provides the kind of balance that includes both divine activity and human responsibility. Let's look at the context for a moment:

So Moses brought Israel from the Red Sea, and they went out into the wilderness of Shur; and they went three days in the wilderness, and found no water. And when they came to Marah, they could not drink of the waters of Marah, for they were bitter; therefore, the name of it was called Marah. And the people murmured against Moses, saying, "What shall we drink?" And he cried unto the Lord; and the Lord shewed him a tree, which when he had cast into the waters, the waters were made sweet; there he made for them a statute and an ordinance, and there he proved them, and said, "If thou wilt diligently hearken to the voice of the Lord thy God, and wilt do that which is right in His sight, and wilt give ear to His commandments, and keep all His statutes, I will put none of these diseases upon thee, which I have brought upon the Egyptians, for I am the Lord that healeth thee" (Ex. 15:22-26).

There can be no doubt that the Bible refers to God healing men physically. But here, as with every other subject referred to in the Scriptures, we must adhere to one of the first rules of interpretation: namely, that *all* the Bible says about a certain subject comprises the doctrine of that subject. When the rule is applied to healing, we find this gracious action of God operating in a context of obedience, and other qualifying factors which are lovingly, instructively, and correctively imposed for our highest good. This principle is true in *both* the Old and New Testaments. Therefore, since Exodus 15 very nearly contains in miniature the whole of biblical revelation on healing, it can be examined as quite representative of all the Bible teaches about the subject.

Two significant phrases should be noted: "If thou wilt...I will" (v. 26). The healing of "the Lord that healeth" is based on an "if." The members of the theocratic nation of Israel were provided with a divinely revealed constitution which covered every aspect of life, both personal and corporate. The Egyptians, with whom the Israelites were contrasted, lived by a code based on human rebellion, demonic idolatry, and self-determinism. The Egyptians were also characterized by "the diseases which God put upon them" as rebels against His government. As the Israelites responded obediently to God's revealed commandments and statutes, they experienced His healing from the diseases common to the Egyptians.

In his book, *The Bible and the Body*,[1] Dr. Roland V. Bingham says, "When God undertook to be the Healer of His people, instead of making unnecessary the observance of health laws, He undertook to instruct His people in the fundamental laws of health. Through Moses He gave the children of Israel the basic principles of health, and placed the nation on a physical plane so advanced that our modern science is only beginning to stumble up to it. The six great laws of health, divinely given, if observed today with the moral law of God, would ensure the healthfulness of any nation submitting to them." He then proceeds to list these laws as 1) *sanitation* (Dt. 23:12-14); 2) *sterilization* (Lev. 11:32, 39-40; Num. 19:11; 31:21-23); 3) *quarantine* (Num. 5:4;

Lev. 13-14); 4)*hygiene* (Lev. 11); 5)*physical culture* [here he observes that "every Israelite was a farmer, whatever else he may be"]; 6) *recuperation* [the sabbath rests]; 7) *the moral law* (Ex. 20:1-17).

His summation of this section is most interesting: "God's method of healing is by the use of natural means to counteract causes; by readjustment to physical laws where, through our ignorance of them or disobedience to them, we have been afflicted; by seeking the benefits of atoning sacrifice where sickness has been caused by sin, and with forgiveness seeking supernatural healing for that which was the result of spiritual causes."

In my own situation, I have no doubt that God added His grace to my obedience to help with my recovery. It is also significant that God *did* effect my healing. He did so, not by a miracle, but by seeing to it that I received proper instruction in my personal responsibilities to fulfill my part in the Covenant. Either way, *my reprieve from the death sentence* was an act of His sovereign grace.

[1]Dr. Roland V. Bingham, *The Bible and the Body*, 4th ed., Toronto, Evangelical Publishers, 1952, pp. 32-38.

8
Reprieve

On June 12, 1979, I felt I had received a sentence of death. In a few days I would have been sixty-five and there I was, lying in a hospital. With few resources to draw on, my body seemed to be systematically deteriorating, and it was only a matter of a short time before the end. What life I had left seemed to offer little more than a continual depressing parade of visits to drugstores, doctor's offices, and hospitals. The daily depression and debilitation caused by diabetes, heart pains, and uncertainty all seemed to add up to a sentence of death, with the execution date drawing ever nearer.

Then, *Reprieve!* It is a word I have constantly used since my remarkable restoration to the health and quality of life I now enjoy. One of the dictionary definitions of the word is "to postpone or remit execution of a condemned person." Within my short twenty-six days at Weimar, the diabetes was gone, and with it, the ever-present paraphernalia of needles, insulin, testing materials, and array of equipment familiar to the diabetic.

As my ailments began to subside both my hope and health began a remarkable journey toward improvement. I knew my sentence was at least under new consideration.

At the final editing of this book it is May, 1983, almost four years since my crisis—and I have not felt this well in years. The angina attacks have disappeared and I often forget to carry my nitroglycerin with me. What's more, I now have zest for living. The old tiredness has given way to a new excitement of activity. I am walking two miles before breakfast, whereas it used to be a chore to get out of bed before mid-morning. Today I feel I am living again. If anyone accuses me of slight giddiness in my exuberance for life, I will gladly plead "guilty," for I face each new day tickled silly just to be alive, feeling good, and still serving my Lord with joy and enthusiasm.

However, I do not claim to have received my glorified body! I am now sixty-nine, and my bodily appearance says "Amen." The hair, what there is left, is still quite gray. The wrinkles still tell their story of the aging process. I must add that I am still a victim of cardiovascular disease and, medically, I could drop dead at any moment. I am under no illusion as to the inevitability of death, but now, by the grace and providence of God, its immediacy is deferred.

My colleagues in the service of the Lord with whom I am so closely related had expressed their concern as they watched the deterioration of my health. I found out later that they had shared among themselves some measure of despair for my life. It was a great joy for me to be able to bring back into our circle of service a renewed life and to experience their love and joy at God's

86

goodness to me. Charles Simpson, Bob Mumford, Don Basham, and Derek Prince have been loyal brothers to me and had patiently endured the added burden of my illness. I am deeply grateful at every remembrance of their love and support.

At the time of this publication I am approaching seventy. Ruth and I travel almost eighty percent of the time, domestically and abroad. Traveling and shuffling schedules is a strenuous and exhausting vocation. My speaking engagements are often full with little break. But we have maintained our new life-style, thanks to Ruth's ingenuity and the kindness of friends around the world. We "carry our kitchen with us," and our bags are never packed without our walking gear, and in my case, my racquetball equipment. My indulgence in racquetball, by the way, has become a bit of a passion. My greatest pleasure in the game is the delight of being able to intimidate some of the "younger brethren" on the courts when I am practically a septuagenarian!

I have been purposefully vague about numerous details of my recovery and present program, since it is not my purpose to promote Weimar or a particular philosophy of nutrition and health. Rather, the emphasis for each of us must be on proper stewardship of our bodies under Christ's lordship, and not on some particular program or regimen. Under the lordship and direction of the Holy Spirit, each will have to deal with the Word of God and his own conscience, and choose a life-style of physical discipline that is pleasing to the Holy Spirit and adequate for his own needs.

The Lord chose a radical program for me, because my situation was critical. Anything less would not have been enough to help me. Even though I would never suggest that everyone needs my extreme program, I would hope and pray everyone would take the time and effort to educate and train themselves in the proper principles of physical care, nutrition, and exercise. To that end, I have added a bibliography of books that will at least provide useful information from which to start further study and, I hope, a new life-style.

As a note of warning, however, I should say that the extreme program which I began was under the supervision of trained medical experts who knew exactly what they were doing. *It would be wise for anyone who is in poor health to find competent medical supervision before embarking on a program of any kind.* Please don't settle for dropping by your local health food store or deciding to follow the homegrown advice of some garden variety food faddist. It could be dangerous.

Interestingly enough, I have encountered a number of people who have actually found "good" excuses for continuing their self-destructive life-style. I decided to include a few of the choice ones for your amusement.

"I don't need to make any changes; I feel great."

So did I when I was young and still heaping up wrath for myself. You won't feel bad until it may be too late! Even then you may not receive the reprieve I was granted. Many men and women drop dead still feeling great.

"My schedule is too busy; I travel too much."

Ruth and I travel about eighty percent of the time and we still follow our disciplines faithfully. You will have to find a better excuse than that.

"All that adjustment to cooking and eating a new way will be too much trouble for my wife."

How much trouble will your wife have adjusting to

88

your premature death? If your wife cares an eyelash for you she will be tickled pink to see you lose weight and lengthen your life—no matter how much trouble it is.

"My children will have a hard time with the adjustment to new foods."

Childhood is the proper time to learn to eat and live right. Train your children now and they will not have the problems we older people do. During the Korean and Vietnam wars, autopsies on teenage soldiers showed well-established signs of arteriosclerosis. It is not just a problem of the "aged." Do your family a favor: Adopt a life-style which will insure your being able to run foot races with your grandchildren.

"My doctor said I am in great health."

Your doctor is probably like many doctors—trained to look for present problems and not potential ones. He may continue to say you are in great health until you are grossly overweight, develop high blood pressure, or start having angina.

"The Scripture says I can eat any deadly thing and it won't hurt me."

That quote is taken so far out of context it is almost too ridiculous to be credited with an answer. God never promised to spare us the effects of our own sinful self-indulgence!

There is really only one honest explanation for not taking better care of our bodies. It is simply that we are too lazy to change our present indulgent life-styles. Our creature comforts are too dear to give up. If that is the case, then may the Lord bless you for your honesty, but I pray you will not need the severe jolt I did to do something before it is too late. I have not written this book just to celebrate my reprieve, but also, I hope, to prod the thousands of my friends and brethren, regardless of age, to begin caring for their bodies in a God-glorifying way, and to know "the abundant life": physically as well as spiritually and mentally.

9
Ruth

Note: I wanted Ruth to be able to share her side of our new life-style. My story could never be complete or have come to as happy an ending without her. She was continually by my side through the years of illness and disability. Her constant love combined with her medical experience kept me from degenerating further than I did.

When we attended Weimar, she made the difference in the Institute being a success or a failure for me. First, she was a constant support and encouragement by her willingness to attend with me. Second, her keen medical knowledge and culinary adeptness enabled her to understand far more of the practical aspects of our new life-style than I ever could have. This enabled us to return home and effectually initiate everything we had learned.

Once we were home, she spent two days rearranging our kitchen and throwing out or giving away foods we would no longer need. She has been a faithful monitor of my eating, making sure only "approved" foods ever pass my lips. Her creativeness and ingenuity in menu planning and meal preparation have made a potentially dull selection of foods a delight to enjoy. Her cleverness in keeping us "on track" while we are traveling has never ceased to amaze me. The faithful and enthusiastic support she has given our new life-style has made the critical difference to me, and I will be eternally grateful for the gift God has given me in her.

E.B.

Looking back over the last four years, my only regret is that the change in our life-style did not happen years earlier. Even though I have never suffered the severe health problems that Ern had, I noticed a marked improvement in my general well-being after we had attended the Institute. My energy level has greatly improved and, whereas I was always too tired or busy to "get a little exercise," I am now more tired and get less done if I don't do several miles of brisk walking and deep breathing each day. When we entered Weimar the tests showed that the triglyceride level of my blood was quite high, even higher than Ern's. It was not causing a problem at the time, but left unchecked for several years, it could have caused serious problems. When we checked out, it was very close to normal.

Of course, the greatest reward I have found from our new life-style is enjoying Ern's new physical health and having watched him progress from a semi-invalid to an enthusiastic and healthful husband. I was grateful to be able to attend the Institute with Ern for a number of other reasons as well.

First, I gained a new understanding of the measures we can take to care for these remarkable God-given instruments, our physical bodies.

Second, it was helpful to Ern for me to be there and learn all I could about initiating and maintaining the drastic changes in our life-style.

Third, I was able to learn much about improving and maintaining my own health.

I must say it is very different not to cook eggs and bacon for breakfast and a big cheeseburger for lunch, and then grill up a juicy steak and all the extras for our supper meal. When I look back on the way we ate, I am amazed that our cholesterol and triglyceride counts were not even higher! For years I had known that I was not cooking the most healthful foods, and periodically I had tried to cut down on the excessive use of oils, sugar, salt, and preservatives.

But I was really just groping in the dark without any real understanding of the basic principles I needed. Now, however, having acquired some knowledge of good nutrition, I feel I have begun to "cook in the light."

It has been a real challenge to totally reorient my food preparation and selection habits, but I confess I enjoy meal preparation more than I ever did before. Instead of my refrigerator being full of butter, cheese, meats, and salad dressings, it is stocked with an abundance of fresh fruits and vegetables. The boxes of cake mixes, processed canned foods, and refined white sugar and flour that once lined my pantry have been replaced by interesting jars of beans, lentils, and grains, as well as a good assortment of whole-grain flours and cereals.

I never before realized the beauty and variety of fruit and vegetable produce! Examine for yourself the kernels of corn on a cob, the petals of an artichoke, the ruby-red color of radishes, the texture of an orange section, and the consistency of a banana. Discover the nutritional value in a potato, a carrot, or an apple. Why mess with all the artificial man-made food products, when our life source is in God and His natural food provisions?

I never thought bread making could be fun. Let me tell you—it is! There are a multitude of things that can be created with bread dough, such as apricot curls, tiny dinner rolls, or even pita bread for pocket sandwiches. I have included one of the bread recipes at the end of this book. It is made without oil, sugar, or white flour, and if you are willing to try it, you will find it very tasty and a satisfying delight.

Building your food intake around grains, legumes, fruits, and vegetables may sound very restrictive, but that is not the case. It is adventuresome and thought-provoking to plan a daily menu and discover the infinite variety of sauces, combinations, soups, and main dishes that can be made to a gourmet's delight with a little time and thought. Along with the bread recipe I have included recipes for "legal" butter, jam, and ketchup.

Numerous government and private studies have recently warned against excessive consumption of red meats. Ern and I have felt we need to abstain from it entirely, and the only meats we eat are occasional small portions of broiled or baked fish or poultry. For those who are traditionally trained in the manner I once was, such a diet sounds frighteningly deficient in protein. We have since learned, however, that there is a wonderful and complete supply of protein available from most of the fifteen hundred different kinds of beans that are available in the world, and the great variety of legumes, the abundance of grains, and all the root crops. God has wonderfully supplied us with protein, and I can assure you, if you know what you are doing, you are in no danger of protein deficiency.

Ern and I are not on a diet. At Weimar we learned that *diet* is a "four-letter word." Diet connotes a special way of eating for a season of time. That is not our case. *We have changed our way of eating permanently and we have no intention of going back to our old ways.*

This style of eating cannot be approached with the typical diet mentality, or it will never work. We must embrace it as a new way of living or we will gradually find ourselves slipping into old habits and patterns and losing all the benefits we had gained.

I have a deep concern to alert and, if necessary, even alarm wives and mothers, since generally speaking they are responsible for what their husbands and families eat. Guarding your family's nutritional well-being is no small task. But without proper nutrition, how will our husbands and children "run the race that is set before us," or even be healthy soldiers in God's army? Are we fulfilling our responsibilities so that we will be able to give a good "account of the deeds done in the body"?

I am writing this not only out of our personal experience but out of concern over the increasing health problems of our country. As Christians we should be leading the way and doing all we can to *prevent* rather than to have to cure bodily ailments. As the adage says, "An ounce of prevention is worth a pound of cure."

True, the life-style we now advocate calls for some personal sacrifice. Mothers, you will forfeit some of the convenience which packaged foods and TV dinners offer. The added time which must be given, first in reorientation and then in additional meal preparation, is no small matter, especially for a working mother or one with small children. But in the long run we must decide if our family's physical well-being is worth the extra time and effort.

Let me urge you to start now, *before* you or your husband have breathing problems, chest pains, abnormal blood counts, extra pounds, diabetes, or any of a number of other life-shortening ailments which are precipitated by our current self-indulgent life-styles. How long will we continue to neglect and abuse these marvelous physical bodies God had given us? How long will we continue to find excuses for withholding from ourselves the diligent care and nurture needed for a life of long and fruitful service to God who created us?

Ruth Baxter

Epilogue

It may have struck some as a bit curious that someone who has spent most of his adult life teaching and preaching the mysteries of the Word of God would take time in the later years of his life to write a book about so earthly a subject as the care of the physical body. Such curiosity probably arises from two sources. One is our habit as Christians of giving a low priority to the importance of the physical body while we occupy ourselves with the more important "things of the Spirit." The other is our ignorance of how much God's Word really does say about the stewardship of our physical bodies.

I was the tragic result of both forms of neglect until—through the critical and frightening experience I have described—the Lord providentially and mercifully delivered me from almost certain premature death and turned me to a far more sensible and biblically balanced life-style. That major adjustment and its impact on my life and the lives of those around me prompted me to publish my story.

More specifically, my reasons for writing this book

were quite simple. First of all, it is an expression of my gratitude to God for the gift of extended life I am presently enjoying. To put it bluntly, had God not providentially intervened and prompted a radical change in my life-style, there is every reason to believe I would be dead today.

Second, I hope my story will sound the alarm for many believers who are, as I once was, neglecting the proper care of their bodies and thus daily moving closer to the inevitable penalty of such neglect. Thousands of sincere, Spirit-filled believers are trudging through life with subnormal energy or debilitating ailments which they are somehow excusing as the normal course of "growing a little older" or "not getting enough rest." The danger is that these little physical "annoyances" are not identified as the forerunner of far more critical physical problems. Many people have succumbed to the mistaken idea that their subnormal physical condition is normal and can only be endured as their health continues to degenerate. In light of my own recent experience, however, I can no longer accept such faulty reasoning. And it is my fervent prayer that the account of my own health crisis will prompt or even shock some readers to take steps to arrest and reverse their current life-styles of deadly self-indulgence.

My third and most urgent burden is to reach Christian young people who have yet to feel the effects of their harmful life-styles. Perhaps it may seem unrealistic to believe that young people who seem so filled with energy, health, and vitality can be persuaded that the blessings of youth are less than eternal. Nonetheless I remain adamant in my determination to discharge my burden in this regard.

While I am concerned for all young people, as a minister I have a special burden for the young men and women who are tomorrow's Christian leaders. It has been my tragic experience personally to watch many of God's choice servants die prematurely due to improper physical care. I have seen men who carried tremendous anointings of power, revelation, and knowledge fall from the race just as they were entering the final and most productive laps of their own course simply because their physical bodies could no longer sustain them. Most of them should not have died when they did. The preventable ailments which claimed their physical lives were the result of unhealthful and negligent habits established in their youth.

During our first few decades of life our bodies seem to have almost limitless powers of recuperation. In those years there seems little outward evidence of the effects of the physical abuse we heap on ourselves. Consequently, we often adopt life-styles deliberately designed to wear out our physical machinery and siphon away our God-given physical reserves.

How much more sensible, healthful, and God-honoring to adopt habits in our youth which reflect our belief that our bodies are indeed "temples of the Holy Spirit," and which will help maintain those bodies at peak efficiency with maximum reserves long after less disciplined individuals have begun to suffer—or even die from the "inevitable" maladies of middle and old age. Even beyond the obvious benefits of a longer and healthier life is the higher motive for the people of God to cross the finish line of life's race in a blaze of strength and glory, rather than stumbling and falling out of the race altogether just when they should be entering their prime.

Originally, I had intended only to give my personal testimony, allowing my experience to have whatever impact it might on those who read the account. By itself that testimony could be dramatic and, I hope, challenging—yet still not provide the depth of motivation which comes from believing and obeying the Scriptures. As a teacher of God's Word I have always followed the principle that "faith comes by hearing, and hearing by the Word of Christ." Why should the source of true obedience be any different when I was teaching about the physical body rather than salvation, baptism, or some other "spiritual" subject? I therefore determined to include what I believe the Bible has to say about the body, trusting that Christians, at least, will not ignore their inspired authority for belief and conduct—no matter how unmoved they might be by my own experience.

Finally, it is clear to me that in recent years we have witnessed a veritable avalanche of public interest in physical fitness, nutrition, exercise, proper rest, and general care of the body. Undoubtedly, much has emerged as a response to the alarming increase in cardiovascular disease and related ailments. Medical authorities have been warning us that these degenerative diseases have increased, at least in part, because of our sedentary life-styles and our poor nutritional habits, both of which are the result of consistently choosing indulgence and immediate self-gratification rather than the long-range benefits which come from self-discipline and moderation.

If proper care and discipline of the body is such a growing concern to unbelievers whose main motivation is self-preservation, how much more diligent ought we

Christians to be in not only professing but also embracing a biblical life-style which calls for specific care of the body based on divinely-revealed requirements. In that way we can prove ourselves faithful stewards of the gift of life given us by God.

Appendix I: Recipes

For those of you who are interested in our present dietary regimen, we have included in the following section a menu guide and sample recipes. Here is an opportunity, with some interesting and tasty dishes, to put into practice some of the changes in eating habits that we have suggested in this book. Although we are not promoting any particular program, we generally follow the nutritional plan of the Weimar Institute which provides for a generous breakfast, a moderate lunch, and a light supper.

*The recipes marked with an asterisk are found in the book, **From the Weimar Kitchen**, which is listed at the end of the section.*

Menu Suggestions

Breakfast—"Eat like a King"
Cereal—cooked whole grain (oats, wheat, rye, millet, etc.); granola
Fresh fruit
Fruit juice (unsweetened) on cereal
Whole grain bread (ripe banana spread on toast is delicious)
If larger breakfast is necessary, a protein dish or bean spread on toast is suggested. (Recipes available in Weimar Cookbook.)

Lunch—"Eat like a Queen"
Entree
Raw vegetables
Yellow or green vegetable
Whole grain bread or potatoes

Supper—"Eat like a Pauper"
Fruit entree, or pudding, etc.
Fresh fruit
Grain—bread, crackers, muffins

Sample Recipes

Breakfast

Whole Wheat Bread *(Makes 2 loaves)*

4   c. very warm water
½   c. chopped dates
2   T. yeast (buy in bulk, as it is much more active)
1   T. salt
½   c. ground sesame seeds (ground walnuts or sunflower seeds can be substituted)
8   c. whole wheat flour (or more)

Whiz dates and 1 cup of water in blender. In large bowl, place remaining 3 cups of water and add date mixture. Sprinkle yeast over mixture and let it react approx. 10-15 minutes in the water. Mix in sesame seeds, salt, and flour. Knead for 15 minutes. Dough should be a little sticky but easy to handle when kneading is finished. Divide dough and place in sprayed loaf pans. Cover with wet cloth and let rise for about 45-60 minutes. (This time period seems to vary.) Bake for 15 minutes at 400°, and then 35-40 minutes at 350°. Air-dry on rack for at least 12 hours after baking. Bread not to be eaten for 24 hours after baking due to working of yeast.

Baked Oatmeal

2½ c. rolled oats
½   c. unsweetened coconut
2   t. vanilla
⅔   c. chopped dates (may be whizzed in blender with a little water)
4   c. water

Mix all ingredients together and bake at 350° for 1 hour. Makes 6 cups. This dish can be frozen and brought out in an emergency.

Peach Crisp

Blend: ½   c. peach juice
         ⅓   c. dates
         ½   t. coriander (spice seasoning)
         ½   banana

105

"I Almost Died!"

Mix with about 4 cups of unsweetened canned
peach slices (drained). Bake at 350° for 30 minutes.
Just before serving, put 1 cup granola on top. May
also be a supper dish.

Granola

1	c. water	Bring to boil,
1	c. dates	blend with
1	t. salt (vege-sal)	banana or
1	t. vanilla	shredded ap-
¼	t. almond extract	ples

½	c. coconut (unsweetened)	Mix dry ingre-
½	c. cornmeal	dients
1	c. rolled wheat (flakes)	
8	c. rolled oats	

Mix thoroughly the date mixture with the dry ingredients. Spread in shallow pans and bake at 200° til
dry, then at 300° for another 20 to 25 minutes.
Watch carefully so it won't burn. Makes 11 cups.
Store in sealed container. Add raisins or dried fruit
as desired after cooking.

Marmalade Deluxe*

1	c. dried apricots (unsulphured)
1	c. pitted dates
1	T. lemon juice (optional)
1¾	c. water or pineapple juice

Wash and soak apricots overnight in liquid. Liquefy in blender or food processor after soaking. Use as jam, jelly, or preserves. Dried pears, peaches, or prunes may be used instead of the apricots, or only a portion may be replaced.

Pineapple Apricot Jam

1¼ c. pitted dried prunes or 1 c. pitted dates
1   c. dried apricots (unsulphured)
½   c. crushed, unsweetened pineapple

Simmer prunes and apricots in juice or water (enough to cover fruit) until soft, or soak overnight. Blend with pineapple in blender until smooth. Keep in refrigerator for about 7-10 days. May freeze.

Fruit Combinations for Jams

1. Dried peaches, banana, water, and a little coconut
2. Dried pears, raisins, water
3. Dried apples, crushed pineapple, and water

Lunch

Great Northern Bean Stew

1½ c. northern beans
1   c. carrots, cut in large chunks
1   c. potatoes, cut in large chunks
½   c. pearl onions

107

"I Almost Died!"

½ c. celery, diced
1   t. salt
1   t. cumin

Soak beans overnight, drain, add vegetables and cook with enough water to cover plus 1 inch. Cook 2-3 hours. Makes 6½ cups. (Flavor improves if made a day or two before using.)

Corn Chowder

1   c. water
⅔ c. diced potato
1   t. onion powder
½ c. chopped celery
⅔ c. whole kernel corn

Blend: 1⅓ c. cooked corn
          ⅔ c. water
          ⅓ t. salt

Mix together & cook for 1 hour or until potatoes are thoroughly cooked. Makes about 4 cups.

Tomato-Lentil Delight*

2   c. uncooked lentils
1   c. chopped onions
½ c. sliced celery
½ c. diced carrot
1   T. dried parsley

108

4   c. tomato sauce
¼   t. sweet basil
1   t. salt
½   c. chopped green pepper

Cook lentils, onions, carrots, and celery together in 4 cups water for ½ hr. Add other ingredients and simmer ½ hr. or until lentils are cooked. Delicious served over whole wheat toast or brown rice.

Carrot-Raisin Salad

5   c. shredded carrots (Food processor chops them nice & fine)
¾   c. raisins
1½   T. concentrated orange juice
2   T. water

Mix together. Makes 5 cups.

Ketchup

3   c. tomato puree
6   T. lemon juice
¾   c. pineapple juice
2   t. salt

Onion powder (good amount) taste
Garlic powder

Makes 4 cups.

Gravy

6   T. whole wheat pastry flour (or unbleached)
2   c. water
½   t. garlic powder
1½   t. onion powder
1/8   t. celery seed
1   t. vegex or soy sauce
¼   c. Mushrooms (sliced)

Simmer, taste to see if more seasonings required.

Garbanzo-Rice Loaf*

1½   c. garbanzo beans (cooked)
1½   c. brown rice (cooked)
¾   c. water
½   c. onion (chopped fine)
1   t. salt
¼   t. garlic powder
1   T. soy sauce
1   c. chopped almonds

Blend garbanzos with water until smooth. Combine all remaining ingredients except rice and blend well. Pour into bowl, add rice, and mix well. Bake as casserole for 30 minutes at 325° covered and for another 30 minutes uncovered.

Supper

Fresh fruit salad and whole wheat toast is an ideal

menu. Other supper recipes:

Millet Pudding

2 c. hot, moist cooked millet
2 c. crushed pineapple (drained)
2-3 bananas (blend only ½ of a banana)
   Fresh, frozen or canned fruit
2 t. vanilla
   Grape Nuts or granola

Blend all ingredients until very smooth, except 2½ bananas, fruit, and Grape Nuts or granola. In shallow baking dish, place ¼" layer of cereal. Pour ½ millet pudding over this, layer sliced bananas followed by remaining pudding. Garnish with fruit. Chill 4-6 hours.

Coconut Date Pie Crust

½ c. chopped dates
¼ c. water
1 c. coconut (fine and unsweetened)
2 T. whole wheat flour

Cook dates in water for about 10-15 minutes. Then puree in blender. Add dates to rest of ingredients and mix well in separate bowl. Put in 9"-10" x ½" pie dish and bake at 350° for 15-20 minutes. Watch carefully. Fill with thickened fruit.

Polynesian Bars

3 c. rolled oats
1 c. whole wheat flour
1 c. unsweetened coconut
⅓ c. chopped nuts
1 c. fresh orange juice

Mix flour, oats, coconut, and nuts. Add orange juice and moisten thoroughly. In a 9″ x 12″ pyrex baking dish, put ½ of this mixture and pat down. Spread filling on this and put rest of oatmeal mixture on top and pat down. Bake at 350° for 30 minutes or until lightly browned.

Filling

2 c. chopped pitted dates
1 20 oz. can unsweetened crushed pineapple

Mix together in saucepan and cook until consistency that can be spread.

Coconut-Whole Wheat Crackers

2 c. whole wheat pastry flour
2 c. fine unsweetened coconut
1 t. salt
1 c. water (or enough to make stiff dough)

Mix all ingredients and knead lightly. Divide dough into 2 balls. Roll out each ball between kitchen

112

towels to a thin dough. If sticky, use more whole wheat flour to keep rolling pin from sticking. Cut into long rectangles and place on cookie sheet (non-stick type) or spray with Pam and wipe off excess before placing crackers on sheet. Bake at 350°, 8-10 minutes. Watch carefully—don't burn!

The following books are highly recommended for further recipe and menu information:

From the Weimar Kitchen. Weimar Institute, P.O. Box A, Weimar, CA. 95736. 1978.

This is the foremost in cookbooks for the serious-minded in nutrition. If any book can be ranked at 100%, this one can. It is a must for any kitchen, with delightful and enjoyable recipies. Make every attempt to get this book.

Brackett, Neva, and Evelyn Earl. *Something Better.* Available from J.E. Brackett, 1402 Valley Heights Road, Billings, MT 59105.

This is an excellent cookbook—one Ruth uses frequently.

*Note: The recipes in this section marked with an asterisk are reprinted from the recommended cookbook, *From the Weimar Kitchen.*

114

Appendix II
Nutrition: An Annotated Bibliography

Heller, Dr. A.L. *Your Body, His Temple.* Nashville: Thomas Nelson, 1981.

This is an excellent book about reaching a balanced Christian view of diet and physical fitness. I recommend it highly.

Pritikin, Nathan. *The Pritikin Program for Diet and Exercise.* New York: Grosset & Dunlap, 1979.

This book transcends fads and cuts right to the heart of how to eat well to live longer, happier, and healthier. Not only is the book full of information, it is written in a very readable style with only 105 pages of narrative. The remainder of the book is devoted to helpful recipes. It is a marvelous primer on the subject of nutrition and a great starting place.

Reuben, David, M.D. *Everything You Always Wanted To Know About Nutrition.* New York: Simon and Schuster, 1978.

The question-and-answer format of this book makes it ideal for the beginner who wishes to familiarize himself with specific topics first. This is an excellent book for the "diehard" and the skeptic who refuse to believe anything is wrong with their present way of eating. Dr. Reuben clearly points out the disastrous nature of the food the majority of Americans eat today. He does this in a lucid and simple style that is quite readable and enjoyable. This book should be high on the list for any who feel self-assured about traditional eating habits.

Duffy, William. *Sugar Blues.* New York: Warner Books, 1976.

This book is a cornerstone work on the history and development of refined sugar and processed foods. Duffy is helpful in exposing the dangers of the "quick and easy" processed foods in our lives, the reluctance of the medical establishment to deal with nutrition, and the historical consequences of changing dietary patterns. The book is written in a very personable style, though the author has a definite prejudice against established religion, especially Christianity. If you can overlook this prejudice, you will gain invaluable knowledge of the history of the decline of modern eating habits and the truth about sugar. This is a reading *must*, second only to Pritikin.

Josephson, Elmer A. *God's Key To Health and Happiness.* Old Tappan, New Jersey: Fleming H. Revell Company, 1976.

Josephson clearly attempts to reestablish the biblical foundations of proper nutrition and eating habits. An especially good book for those "liberated" Christians who think that God does not have anything to say about what we eat—the author cleverly answers many objections. Though excellent in his theology of eating and with many good suggestions, Josephson is a bit too general in application of how to eat, not cutting deeply enough (as Pritikin does). The author makes profound contributions to the understanding of "live foods"; however, he doesn't use discretion in the matter of brown sugar, oil, and molasses (which I believe are big "no-no's"). A book well worth reading, it should be appropriately ranked behind Pritikin and *Sugar Blues* in reading priority.

Lappe, Frances Moore. *Diet for A Small Planet.* New York: Ballantine Books, 1975.

This work is more of a moral book than a purely nutritional book. What Mrs. Lappe has to say about the excess and unprincipled abuse of protein in our culture is well worth hearing. Not only does she introduce the reader to protein abuse; she gives a helpful theory of proper usage in diet. The book is approximately 160 pages of narrative. This is not a must in reading, but for the overachiever, or one with spare time, it might possibly be worth your while.

Williams, Dr. Roger J. *Nutrition Against Disease.* New York: Bantam Books, 1973.

Dr. Williams is one of the foremost scientists in the field of vitamin research—in fact he is the discoverer of one of the B-complex vitamins. His book is well written and well documented, yet very intense. The author's hypothesis is that good nutrition is not merely a matter of "eating right"; he believes there are genetic characteristics in nutrition which are special to each individual. He offers some interesting thoughts on the nutritional chain of life, and provides a wealth of information about the effects of nutrition in a number of diseases (including important information for pregnant women). The book is intriguing, but falls short of clear-cut recommendations, like those found in Pritikin. Interesting reading, but only for the serious student.

Leonard, Jon N., J. L. Hofer, and N. Pritikin. *Live Longer Now.* New York: Grosset & Dunlap, 1974.

This book is actually a precursor of *The Pritikin Program for Diet and Exercise.* Well written and full of important, fundamental nutritional facts, it is an excellent supplement to the Pritikin book.

Adams, Ruth, and Frank Murray. *The Good Seeds, The Rich Grains, The Hard Nuts for Healthier, Happier Life.* New York: Larchmont Books, 1973.

As the title might suggest, the authors seemingly did not know where to stop! As literature this is probably one of the worst written books in the field. The style is both patchwork and inconsistent. Ideologically, the book typifies the negative stereotype of the "health food junkie." Absolutely no discretion is advised in eating habits, except that the food prescribed is better for you. The basic philosophy is "If you eat too much of this, you need to eat some of this, or take vitamins." The authors' mentality is nonsensical and the result is confusion. The only redeeming value is encyclopedic. It is a good source book, telling the origins and attributes of the various nuts, grains, and seeds.

Exercise and Your Heart.Consumer Information Center, Department P, Pueblo, Colorado 81009.

The free booklet is especially helpful in getting

those who are inactive involved in exercise. It gives good advice on the types of exercise that are good for your heart, as well as those of no value. Also included is a guide to help the individual get started and pace himself. Very worthwhile, and it's free!

Dworkin, Floss and Stan. *Bake Your Own Bread and Be Healthier.* New York: Holt, Rinehart and Winston, 1972.
This is primarily a source book for baking bread. It contains loads of valuable information on grains and baking. If used wisely, it could be very helpful. A caution is necessary because of the book's allowance of unbleached white flour, eggs, and excessive use of honey and vegetable oil.

About the Author

Ern Baxter is a veteran minister of the gospel, having served extensively throughout Canada, England, and the United States. Ern is the author of *Life on Wings* and *Thy Kingdom Come*, which are available through: Integrity House, P.O. Box Z, Mobile, AL 36616.

He presently serves as a pastor in Gulf Coast Covenant Church in Mobile, Alabama, where he resides with his wife, Ruth. He also travels internationally as a conference speaker. Articles by Ern are regularly featured in *New Wine* Magazine, which is also available by writing the address above.